EUROPEAN COMMISSION

DIRECTORATE-GENERAL
FOR EMPLOYMENT,
INDUSTRIAL RELATIONS
AND SOCIAL AFFAIRS

C000010845

Public
and saf
at work

Non-ionizing radiation

Sources, exposure
and health effects

Published by the
EUROPEAN COMMISSION

Directorate-General V
Employment, Industrial Relations and Social Affairs

B-1049 Brussels

LEGAL NOTICE

Neither the European Commission nor any person acting on behalf of
the Commission is responsible for the use which might be made of the
following information

Cataloguing data can be found at the end of this publication

Luxembourg: Office for Official Publications of the European Communities, 1996

ISBN 92-827-5492-8

Preface

This report was commissioned and partly funded by Directorate General V of the European Commission to provide information about sources of non-ionising radiation (NIR) to which the general public might be exposed, to provide an overview of the biology, epidemiology and exposure assessment related to these sources, to summarise guidelines and standards for limiting exposure that are relevant to the member states of the European Union and to make recommendations in respect of research and other relevant initiatives.

In this report NIR has been subdivided into the following spectral regions:

- static and slowly time varying (less than a few hertz (Hz)) electromagnetic fields
- time varying electromagnetic fields of frequencies less than 100 kHz
- electromagnetic fields and radiation of frequencies between 100 kHz and 300 GHz
- infrared radiation (IRR)
- visible radiation (light)
- ultraviolet radiation (UVR)

The levels of electromagnetic fields and radiation to which people may be exposed were, until the beginning of this century, very low. Modern industrial development has resulted in increasing levels of exposure to people to a complex mix of artificially elevated electromagnetic fields that span a wide frequency range. One of the most significant contributions to this changing environment has been the technological advances associated with the growth of electrical power generation and transmission systems and their use in homes and workplaces. In addition, electromagnetic field generating devices have proliferated in telecommunications and broadcasting, in industrial workplaces, offices, public transportation systems, homes, cars and elsewhere. Increased exposure of people to UVR has also occurred. This has resulted from changes in social conditions and personal behaviour, particularly in respect of elective exposure.

In recent years, concern has increased about possible health effects that might result from exposure to NIR and particularly about cancer.

The results of epidemiological studies investigating possible correlations between cancer and exposure to electromagnetic fields and radiation have yielded equivocal results. They point to an association between cancer and electromagnetic field exposure, which is sufficiently indicative to merit further research, but fall short of determining causation. In contrast, rising rates of skin cancer in Europe and elsewhere in white populations, have stimulated health initiatives in a number of countries to try to arrest these increases. The results of epidemiological, clinical and biological studies point strongly to solar ultraviolet radiation exposure as a causative agent for skin cancer and for cataract.

A summary and extended technical summary are provided.

The report was compiled by an *ad hoc* working group comprising scientists from; the National Radiological Protection Board (NRPB), United Kingdom; the Bundesamt für Strahlenschutz (BfS), Germany; and the Istituto Superiore di Sanità (ISS), Italy.

i

Exposure of the Public to Non-ionising Radiation

Ad Hoc Working Group

Coordinator and editor

Dr A F McKinlay
National Radiological Protection Board, United Kingdom

Members

Mr S G Allen
National Radiological Protection Board, United Kingdom

Professor J H Bernhardt
Bundesamt für Strahlenschutz, Germany

Dr C M H Driscoll
National Radiological Protection Board, United Kingdom

Professor M Grandolfo,
Istituto Superiore di Sanità, Italy

Dr S M Mann
National Radiological Protection Board, United Kingdom

Dr G F Mariutti
Istituto Superiore di Sanità, Italy

Dipl-Ing R Matthes
Bundesamt für Strahlenschutz, Germany

Dr R D Saunders
National Radiological Protection Board, United Kingdom

Dr P Vecchia
Istituto Superiore di Sanità, Italy

Acknowledgements

On behalf of the *Ad Hoc* Working Group, The Editor gratefully acknowledges the assistance of: Dr G Gouvras, Mrs M T van der Venne, Dr J-C Berger and Dr K Runeberg, Directorate General V of the European Commission, and Dr J Stather, NRPB, in providing scientific comments on the report: Mrs Jean Stirrup, NRPB Typing Unit Manager and her staff: Ms A Sharma, NRPB Publications and: Mrs A Purling, NRPB Non-ionising Radiation Department.

Contents

Page

Summary   1

Technical Summary   3

1   Physical interaction of non-ionising electromagnetic fields and radiation
    with people   3
2   Sources and exposure   4
3   Biological effects   6
4   Human health studies   9
5   Hazard assessment   11
6   National and international standards of protection
    against electromagnetic fields and radiation   13
7   Recommendations   14

1   Introduction   17

2   Physical interaction of non-ionising electromagnetic fields and radiation
    with people   19

    2.1   Static and slowly time varying fields   19
          2.1.1   Electric fields   19
          2.1.2   Magnetic fields   19

    2.2   Time varying electromagnetic fields of frequencies less than 100 kHz   20
          2.2.1   Electric fields   20
          2.2.2   Magnetic fields   21

    2.3   Electromagnetic fields and radiation of frequencies between 100 kHz
          and 300 GHz   21

    2.4   Optical radiation   25

    2.5   Summary   27
          2.5.1   Static and slowly time varying fields   27
          2.5.2   Time varying electromagnetic fields of frequencies
                  less than 100 kHz   28
          2.5.3   Electromagnetic fields and radiation of frequencies
                  between 100 kHz and 300 GHz   28
          2.5.4   Optical radiation   29

    References   30

3   Sources and exposure   31

    3.1   Static and slowly time varying fields   31
          3.1.1   Electric fields   31
          3.1.2   Magnetic fields   32

    3.2   Time varying electromagnetic fields of frequencies less than 100 kHz   33
          3.2.1   Electric fields   33
          3.2.2   Magnetic fields   36

    3.3   Electromagnetic fields and radiation of frequencies between 100 kHz
          and 300 GHz   43
          3.3.1   Background and terminology   43
          3.3.2   Broadcast transmitters   45

	3.3.3	Cellular radio	46
	3.3.4	Citizens band radio	51
	3.3.5	Communications links	53
	3.3.6	Radar	55
	3.3.7	Microwave ovens	57

| 3.4 | Visible and infrared radiation | | 57 |

3.5	Ultraviolet radiation		61
	3.5.1	Solar radiation	61
	3.5.2	Lamps	61
	3.5.3	Gas and arc welding	66
	3.5.4	Lasers	67

3.6	Summary		68
	3.6.1	Static and slowly time varying fields	68
	3.6.2	Time varying electromagnetic fields of frequencies less than 100 kHz	68
	3.6.3	Electromagnetic fields and radiation of frequencies between 100 kHz and 300 GHz	68
	3.6.4	Optical radiation	68

| | References | | 69 |

| 4 | Biological effects | | 72 |

4.1	Static and slowly time varying fields		72
	4.1.1	Electric fields	72
	4.1.2	Magnetic fields	73

4.2	Time varying electric and magnetic fields of frequencies less than 100 kHz		74
	4.2.1	Electric fields – studies on volunteers	74
	4.2.2	Magnetic fields – studies on volunteers	78
	4.2.3	Effects on circadian rhythms and melatonin secretion	80
	4.2.4	Reproductive and developmental effects	80
	4.2.5	Carcinogenesis	82
	4.2.6	Immune system responses	84
	4.2.7	Frequency/amplitude specific effects	84

4.3	Electromagnetic fields and radiation of frequencies between 100 kHz and 300 GHz		84
	4.3.1	Studies on volunteers	85
	4.3.2	Nervous system	86
	4.3.3	Endocrine system	86
	4.3.4	Haematopoietic and immune system	86
	4.3.5	Ocular effects	87
	4.3.6	Cardiovascular system	87
	4.3.7	Behaviour	87
	4.3.8	Reproduction and development	88
	4.3.9	Genetic effects	88
	4.3.10	Cancer-related studies	88
	4.3.11	Auditory perception	89
	4.3.12	Indirect effects	89

4.4	Optical radiation		89
	4.4.1	Ultraviolet radiation	89
	4.4.2	Effects of non-laser optical radiation on the retina	96

| | | 4.4.3 | Effects of laser radiation | 97 |

	4.5	Summary		99
		4.5.1	Static and slowly time varying fields	99
		4.5.2	Time varying electric and magnetic fields of frequencies less than 100 kHz	99
		4.5.3	Electromagnetic fields and radiation of frequencies between 100 kHz and 300 GHz	99
		4.5.4	Optical radiation	100

References 101

5   Human health studies   **107**

5.1   Static fields   107

5.2   Time varying electromagnetic fields of frequencies
      less than 100 kHz   107
      5.2.1   Cancer   107
      5.2.2   General effects on health   111

5.3   Electromagnetic fields and radiation of frequencies between
      100 kHz and 300 GHz   112
      5.3.1   Pregnancy outcome and reproduction studies   113
      5.3.2   Cancer   113
      5.3.3   Cataracts   114
      5.3.4   General effects on health   114

5.4   Optical radiation   115
      5.4.1   Ultraviolet radiation   115
      5.4.2   Visible and infrared radiation   120

5.5   Summary   121
      5.5.1   Time varying electromagnetic fields of frequencies
              of less than 100 kHz   121
      5.5.2   Electromagnetic fields and radiation of frequencies between
              100 kHz and 300 GHz   121
      5.5.3   Optical radiation   121

References 122

6   Hazard assessment   **128**

6.1   Static and slowly time varying fields   128
      6.1.1   Electric fields   128
      6.1.2   Magnetic fields   128

6.2   Time varying electromagnetic fields of frequencies less
      than 100 kHz   129
      6.2.1   Electric fields   129
      6.2.2   Magnetic fields   130

6.3   Electromagnetic fields and radiation of frequencies between
      100 kHz and 300 GHz   131

6.4   Visible and infrared radiation   133
      6.4.1   Solar radiation   133
      6.4.2   Emissions from other sources   133

	6.5	Ultraviolet radiation	134
		6.5.1 Solar radiation	134
		6.5.2 Lighting systems	135
		6.5.3 Medical sources	135
		6.5.4 Welding	136
	6.6	Laser radiation	136
		6.6.1 Lasers used for display and entertainment purposes	136
		6.6.2 Medical lasers	138
		6.6.3 Lasers used in the `beauty' industry	138
		6.6.4 Lasers used in compact disc (CD) players	138
		6.6.5 Lasers used in bar code readers	138
		6.6.6 Lasers used in other areas	138
	6.7	Summary	139
		6.7.1 Static and slowly time varying fields	139
		6.7.2 Time varying electromagnetic fields of frequencies less than 100 kHz	139
		6.7.3 Electromagnetic fields and radiation of frequencies between 100 kHz and 300 GHz	140
		6.7.4 Optical radiation	141
	References		141
7	**International and European Union Member States, guidelines and regulations for protection against NIR**		**144**
	7.1	International	144
		7.1.1 Static fields	145
		7.1.2 50/60 Hz electric and magnetic fields	145
		7.1.3 Electromagnetic fields and radiation of frequencies between 100 kHz and 300 GHz	146
		7.1.4 Ultraviolet radiation	147
		7.1.5 Infrared radiation	150
	7.2	National	150
		7.2.1 Electromagnetic fields and radiation	150
	7.3	Summary	155
	References		155
8	**Conclusions and recommendations**		**157**
	8.1	Biological research	157
		8.1.1 Static and slowly time varying electric and magnetic fields	157
		8.1.2 Time varying electromagnetic fields of frequencies less than 100 kHz	157
		8.1.3 Electromagnetic fields and radiation of frequencies between 100 kHz and 300 GHz	158
		8.1.4 Optical radiation	159
	8.2	Epidemiological research	160
		8.2.1 Electromagnetic fields and radiation	160
		8.2.2 Optical radiation	160

8.3	Exposure and dosimetry research	161
	8.3.1 Electromagnetic fields and radiation	161
	8.3.2 Optical radiation	162
8.4	Standards development	163

Summary

The subject of this report is electromagnetic non-ionising radiation (NIR), the sources of NIR in the public domain, the levels of NIR to which the general public are likely to be exposed and the significance of the exposures to health. Recommendations for research are provided.

Electromagnetic NIR includes, static and time varying electromagnetic fields and radiofrequency (RF) radiation, infrared radiation (IRR, heat), visible radiation (light) and ultraviolet radiation (UVR). The manner in which these different fields and radiations interact with people is quite different and the assessment of potential hazards is not a simple matter but requires precise measurements and interpretation by skilled professionals.

With respect to detrimental health effects, the NIR that results in the most significant exposure of members of the general public is ultraviolet radiation, resulting mainly from elective exposure to the sun. There is convincing evidence from biological and from human health (epidemiological) studies that exposure to the sun is a major risk factor in skin cancer and may play a role in the onset of cataract. Depending on individual circumstances, other sources of UVR, such as sunbeds and some unshielded lamps and arcs, may also contribute to an individual's risk, but generally to a much lesser extent than sun exposure. Lasers, used in the public domain for display and entertainment purposes, are capable of injuring the eye.

The general public are unlikely to be exposed to levels of electromagnetic fields and radiation capable of causing established direct acute effects such as electrical nerve stimulation, at electricity supply frequency, or heating at radiofrequencies. Severe indirect effects, such as painful electric shock and RF burns caused by touching metallic objects in the field, are also unlikely to occur to the general public. However, strong fields may interfere with implanted medical devices (for example, unipolar cardiac pacemakers) and cause malfunction. International and national protection guidelines exist to prevent both direct and indirect effects by providing exposure limits that should be adhered to by the operators of sources giving rise to electromagnetic fields. A number of European countries have begun to draft legislation setting limits on NIR exposure and there may be a future need to harmonize these.

There is no clear evidence that exposure to electromagnetic fields and radiation results in an increased risk of cancer. Whereas biological studies have demonstrated that UVR can damage DNA directly and thereby initiate cancer, there is no such evidence in relation to electromagnetic fields. Neither is there persuasive evidence that electromagnetic fields can promote the development of cancer.

Some human health (epidemiological) studies have demonstrated associations between electromagnetic fields and cancer, however, several international and national expert scientific groups who have examined the results of such studies, together with the biological evidence, have concluded that they do not satisfactorily demonstrate that electromagnetic fields can cause cancer and that currently available epidemiological data do not provide a basis for setting exposure limits.

The recommendations in this report reflect the need for biological, epidemiological and dosimetry research in two important areas; ultraviolet radiation, where adverse health effects including cancer are well established, although there is little public concern and; electromagnetic fields and radiation, where the evidence for carcinogenesis is weak and inconclusive, but conversely there is considerable public concern. It is recommended that the research should be carried out as part of a focused and coordinated programme of work within the European Union, by identifying appropriate studies, establishing agreed experimental protocols and performing appropriate statistical analyses.

The fruits of such research are scientific data and information that can be used to identify and quantify risks and, where appropriate, to point to cost effective health strategies to reduce risks. There is a need to provide factual information about the established risks of exposure to non-ionising radiation to policy makers, the media and directly to the general public.

Technical Summary

1 Physical interaction of non-ionising electromagnetic radiation with people

Static and slowly time varying fields

Static electric fields induce electric charges on the surface of an object. These charges may cause forces on, for example, body hair, which may be perceived. Additionally, discharges can occur when people and metal objects come into close proximity.

Static magnetic fields interact with living matter through three established physical mechanisms: magnetic induction (electrodynamic interactions with moving electrolytes and Faraday currents), magnetomechanical effects (most important are force effects on ferromagnetic materials) and electronic interactions. Strong static magnetic fields may interfere with implanted medical devices and cause malfunction.

Time varying electromagnetic fields of frequencies of less than 100 kHz

Since time-dependent electric fields induce a surface charge on an exposed body, varying with frequency, this results in currents inside the body. For sinusoidal electric fields the magnitude of the currents inside the body increases proportionally with frequency. Magnetic fields act on people by inducing electric fields and circulating currents inside the body. The current density ($A\ m^{-2}$) increases with frequency and magnetic flux density amplitude, and also with tissue conductivity and inductive loop radius.

Indirect coupling mechanisms are also of importance. Electromagnetic fields coupling to a conductor cause electric currents to pass through the body of a person in contact with it. Transient discharges (often called microshocks) can occur when people and metal objects exposed to a sufficiently strong electric field come into close proximity. Electric and magnetic fields may interfere with implanted medical devices and cause malfunction.

Electromagnetic fields and radiation of frequencies between 100 kHz and 300 GHz

Source charges or currents oscillate at frequencies in the radiofrequency and microwave range, and electric and magnetic fields produced by these sources will radiate from them. A convenient and commonly used description of this radiation is wave propagation (far-field). The region close to a source is called the near-field. In this region the electric and magnetic fields are often non-propagating in nature and are sometimes referred to as fringing fields or reactive near-fields. In this case, objects located near sources may strongly affect the nature of the fields.

Radiofrequency and microwave fields and waves induce electric fields and corresponding electric currents in exposed biological systems. The intensities and spatial distribution of induced currents are dependent on various characteristics of the exposure field and geometry, and the exposed biological system, ie, its size, geometry, and electric properties. When interactions are due to the rate of energy deposition per unit mass, the dosimetric quantity specific energy absorption rate (SAR) is used, most often expressed in watts per kilogram ($W\ kg^{-1}$).

Whole-body SAR is strongly dependent on frequency and the orientation of the electric field relative to the longest dimension of the body. The highest rate of energy deposition occurs for frequencies such that the major length is approximately 0.36 to 0.40 times the free-space wavelength of the radiation. For an adult human this corresponds approximately to a frequency range of some tens of MHz. For near-fields, SARs considerably lower than those for far-field exposure conditions are observed.

Optical radiation

Optical radiation comprises ultraviolet radiation (UVR), visible radiation and infrared radiation (IRR) and by convention is considered to be the part of the electromagnetic spectrum covering the wavelength range 10 or 100 nm to 1 mm. Radiation of wavelengths below 180 nm is strongly absorbed in air and therefore does not represent any direct radiation hazard. The natural (solar) optical spectrum at the Earth's surface extends from about 290 nm to 1 mm. Radiation of wavelengths below about 290 m is absorbed in the earth's atmosphere.

Lasers are unique in that they are capable of emitting optical radiation at essentially one wavelength. All other optical sources emit the radiation as a spectral continuum typically containing peaks and troughs. Because of the great dependence of the type and magnitude of biological (including hazardous) effects on the wavelength of the radiation it is important to have information about the spectral emissions of such sources. For hazard analysis the most useful information is a set of data comprising spectral irradiance ($W m^{-2} nm^{-1}$) measurements of the source emissions at the target. The (total) irradiance ($W m^{-2}$) can be obtained by simply summing over all wavelengths of interest.

2   Sources and exposure

Static and slowly time varying fields

Static and slowly time varying (frequencies less than a few Hz) electric fields can reach field strengths of the order of tens of $kV m^{-1}$ from both natural and artificial sources. Static and slowly time varying magnetic fields are also naturally occurring. In general, the earth's magnetic field is dominant in this frequency range. Natural magnetic field strengths are only exceeded in certain situations, for example inside some direct current (DC) driven public transportation systems. There, magnetic flux densities can reach values of up to 10 mT.

Time varying electromagnetic fields of frequencies less than 100 kHz

In the frequency range below 100 kHz the dominant exposure of the general public results from the use of electric power. The main frequency in Europe for this purpose is 50 Hz.

Significant exposure to electric fields is only possible in the vicinity of high voltage overhead transmission lines. Depending on the distance to the line and the line voltage, field strengths of up to about 7 $kV m^{-1}$ are possible.

Magnetic field exposures for the general public measured on an individual basis in general range between about 10 and 300 nT. People living within 100 m or so of high voltage transmission lines may be exposed to the higher end of this range of magnetic fields and above.

Near electrical appliances, magnetic fields may vary up to the order of a few mT or more, but local variability of such fields is very high. Thus field strengths reduce quickly with increasing distance to the source.

Electromagnetic fields and radiation of frequencies between 100 kHz and 300 GHz

The principal sources of electromagnetic fields and radiation in this frequency range relevant to exposure of the general public are those associated with telecommunications and radar, table TS.1.

VLF and MF broadcast antennas can produce the most significant exposure of the general public to radiofrequency radiation although the sites are relatively large and access restricted. Several hundred $V m^{-1}$ at distances up to 30 m are typical. Antennas used for television and radio

4

at VHF and UHF frequencies should not usually give rise to significant general public exposure. Maximum field strengths to which the general public might normally be exposed are a few V m^{-1}.

Table TS.1 Sources of electromagnetic fields and radiation and their emissions

Frequency	Wavelength	Description	Band	Sources
0 Hz		Static		Earth's field
				Magnets, DC supplies
		Sub-extremely low frequency	SELF	
30 Hz	10 000 km			Electric power lines and
50 Hz	6 000 km	Extremely low frequency	ELF	cables. Domestic and
300 Hz	1 000 km			industrial appliances
				Induction heaters
		Voice frequency*	VF	
3 kHz	100 km			
		Very low frequency	VLF	Television sets
				Visual display units
30 kHz	10 km			
		Low frequency	LF	AM radio
300 kHz	1 km			
				Induction heaters
		Medium frequency	MF	
3 MHz	100 m			
				RF heat sealers
		High frequency	HF	
30 MHz	10 m			
				FM radio
		Very high frequency	VHF	
300 MHz	1 m			
				Cellular telephones
		Ultra high frequency	UHF	Television broadcast
				Microwave ovens
3 GHz	10 cm			
		Super high frequency	SHF	Radar
				Satellite links
30 GHz	1 cm			Microwave communications
		Extra high frequency	EHF	Point-to-point links
300 GHz	1 mm			
		Infrared		

* Radiofrequencies equivalent to speech (sound) frequencies
Note 1000 Hz = 1 kHz; 1000 kHz = 1 MHz; 1000 MHz = 1 GHz

5

Cellular base stations can potentially produce fields of tens of V m^{-1} at distances up to 60 m or so if all of their channels operate simultaneously at full power. This is highly unlikely to ever occur in practice. Measurements suggest that fields to which the public may be exposed in practice would be considerably below 10 V m^{-1}. Mobile transmitters on cars can generate fields of several hundred V m^{-1} at distances less than 10 cm; however, fields inside the vehicles are less than 30 V m^{-1}.

Radar installations can produce power densities greater than 100 W m^{-2} in their main beams but, when radars are rotating, the average root mean square (RMS) power at an exposure position will be reduced by a factor of around 100.

Optical radiation

Exposure of the general public to optical radiation is dominated by the sun, although high power optical sources such as lasers and sunbeds are increasingly being used in the public environment. Table TS.2 lists some optical sources and their emissions relevant to exposure of the general public.

For most people the major source of UVR exposure is the sun. However, for some individuals, for at least some of the time, UVR from artificial sources may contribute significantly to their total exposure. Such sources include those used for medical therapy, cosmetic tanning and a few industrial sources.

Incandescent sources such as tungsten filament bulbs generally emit levels of UVR insignificant to human health, although some unshielded tungsten halogen lamps can emit amounts of UVR sufficient to cause erythema.

General lighting fluorescent lamps are specifically designed to emit light and only very small amounts of UVR are produced at the levels of light exposure normally encountered in the home. However, special application fluorescent lamps, such as those used for medical purposes and for cosmetic tanning, emit levels of UVR sufficient to cause skin and eye injury. The most potent artificial sources of UVR, and particularly of UVB and UVC, are those characterised as high intensity discharge (HID) lamps. These include high pressure mercury, mercury metal halide and xenon lamps. HID lamps used for lighting purposes are double envelope lamps whose outer envelope attenuates the UVR emitted and, when used within properly designed luminaires, do not represent a UVR hazard. Any HID lamp used in an open situation without secondary containment is likely to constitute a UVR hazard.

Gas welding, brazing and cutting processes operate at temperatures insufficiently high to cause the emission of intense UVR, although at close distances and for long exposure times, advised limits for protection may be approached and possibly exceeded. Light and IRR present a potential hazard to the eyes. Arc welding processes are particularly potent sources of UVR and even very short exposures may be hazardous to the eyes and to the skin of the operator and of any onlooker. They also emit light and IRR hazardous to the retina even when viewed at some distance from the source. Appropriate controls need to be applied when such processes are carried out in a public area.

3   Biological effects

Static and slowly time varying electric and magnetic fields

The few experimental studies that have been carried out of the biological effects of static electric fields provide no evidence to suggest the existence of any adverse effect on human health.

For most people, the annoying perception of surface electric charge, acting directly on the surface of the body, will not occur during exposure to static electric fields of less than about 25 kV m^{-1}.

Table TS.2 Sources of optical radiation and their emissions

Wavelength	Band	Sources
	UVC	Germicidal lamps Welding arcs
280 nm	———	
	UVB	Sun Sunbeds Unshielded tungsten halogen lamps Welding arcs
315 nm	———	
	UVA	Black lights Fluorescent lighting Insect lures Medical lamps Sun Sunbeds Tungsten halogen lamps Welding arcs
380/400 nm	———	
	VISIBLE	Display lasers General lighting lamps Medical lamps and lasers Photocopiers Sun Welding and brazing
760/780 nm	———	
	IRA	IRR heating and cooking lamps Medical lasers Sun Welding and brazing
1400 nm	———	
	IRB	IRR heating and cooking lamps Sun
3 μm	———	
	IRC	Medical lasers Sun
1 mm	———	

7

There is no direct experimental evidence of any acute adverse effect on human health from exposure to static magnetic fields of up to 2 T. There is less information on the effects of chronic exposure but so far, no long-term effects have become apparent.

Time varying electric and magnetic fields of frequencies less than 100 kHz

It is well established that exposure to electric and magnetic fields results in the induction of electric fields and currents in biological tissues, and may result in a variety of nervous system responses. A threshold current density of 10 mA m^{-2} for fields of frequency between 10 Hz and 1 kHz can be conservatively estimated for weak effects on central nervous system activity. Few studies have been performed with volunteers, and the most consistent response other than the appearance of magnetic phosphenes appears to be a minor reduction in heart rate observed immediately during or after exposure to a combined electric and magnetic field. The small magnitude and transitory nature of this effect, however, does not suggest a health risk.

Most biological studies suggest that exposure to low frequency electric and magnetic fields does not have any significant effects on mammalian development. Similarly, there is no persuasive evidence that ELF electromagnetic fields are able to influence any of the accepted stages in carcinogenesis. Effects on initiation are extremely unlikely suggesting that if there is an effect it will be at the level of promotion or progression. Here, the evidence remains confused, but with no clearly reproducible effects apparent.

Electromagnetic fields and radiation of frequencies between 100 kHz and 300 GHz

Many of the biological effects of acute exposure to electromagnetic fields and radiation are consistent with responses to induced heating, resulting in rises in tissue or body temperature of about 1°C or more. Most responses have been reported at SARs above about 1 to 2 W kg^{-1} in different animal species exposed under various environmental conditions. These animal (particularly primate) data indicate the types of responses that are likely to occur in humans subjected to a sufficient heat load. However, direct quantitative extrapolation to humans is difficult given species differences in responses in general, and in thermoregulatory ability in particular.

The most sensitive animal responses to heat loads are thermoregulatory adjustments, such as reduced metabolic heat production and vasodilation, with thresholds ranging between about 0.5 and 5 W kg^{-1}, depending on environmental conditions. However, these reactions form part of the natural repertoire of thermoregulatory responses that serve to maintain normal body temperatures. Transient effects seen in exposed animals which are consistent with responses to increases in body temperature of 1°C or more (and/or SARs in excess of about 2 W kg^{-1} in primates and rats) include reduced performance of learned tasks and increased plasma corticosteroid levels.

Most animal data indicate that implantation of the embryo and the development of the fetus are unlikely to be affected by exposures which increase maternal body temperature by less than 1°C.

Above this temperature, adverse effects, such as growth retardation and post-natal changes in behaviour may occur, with more severe effects occurring at higher maternal temperatures.

Most animal data suggest that radiofrequency (RF) exposure low enough to keep body temperature within the normal physiological range is not mutagenic. Such exposure will not result in somatic mutation nor in hereditary effects.

There is much less information describing the effects of chronic low level exposure. So far, however, it is not apparent that there are any long-term effects which can result from exposures below thermally significant levels.

The possibility that exposure to RF fields might influence the process of carcinogenesis is of particular concern. So far, there is no definite evidence that irradiation does have an effect.

Many experimental data indicate that RF fields are not mutagenic, and so they are unlikely to act as initiators of carcinogenesis; the few studies carried out have looked mostly for evidence of an enhancement of the effect of a known carcinogen.

Optical radiation

Because of the limited penetration of optical radiation in body tissues, the adverse health effects are limited mainly to the skin and the eyes, although systemic effects are also possible. The effects are strongly wavelength dependent, with photochemical effects dominating at shorter optical wavelengths, especially in the ultraviolet region, and thermal effects dominating at longer wavelengths, principally in the infrared region.

Effects on human skin include acute UVR-induced erythema, skin cancers, photoaging and heating as well as UVR-induced localised responses affecting the immune function of the skin. Effects on the eye include acute UVR-induced corneal (photokeratitis) and conjunctival effects, UVR and thermal-induced changes in the lens possibly leading to cataract, and photochemical and thermal effects on the retina. Pulsed laser radiation produces additional effects characterised by very rapid absorption of energy by tissue.

Exposure of the general public is dominated by solar radiation even though the contribution from artificial sources has increased significantly over the past 30 years or so. Solar radiation exposure is clearly implicated in the increased incidence of skin cancer. A quantitative evaluation of risk for the induction of skin cancer requires a dose-response relationship to be established. The dose-response relationship and the carcinogenic potential of UVR for the induction of non-melanoma skin cancer in mice have been established but there are as yet few data relevant to the spectral effectiveness of UVR for the induction of malignant melanoma.

UVR can induce local or systemic responses by affecting the immunological function of the skin. The skin contains Langerhans cells, keratinocytes and T cells, the cellular components of the peripheral immune system. Experimental work on animals has shown that low level exposure to UVR impairs the immune surveillance system at the site of the exposure and higher levels of exposure suppress the immune system elsewhere also. These effects could have important implications with respect to human health.

Cataract is a multifactorial disease related to the natural aging process. There is evidence that ultraviolet radiation can play a role in its onset and temporal progression. Long-term exposure to infrared radiation can also lead to lens opacification (infrared cataract).

Optical radiation in the spectral region approximately 400–1400 nm is transmitted through the anterior media of the eye and focused, principally by the air/corneal interface, onto the retina. Photochemical retinal injury can result from sufficiently high exposure to visible radiation with a strong blue-light component. The degree of injury is related to the total energy absorbed. Thermal retinal lesions may occur as the result of exposure to very high radiance sources such as a high power laser.

4   Human health studies

Static and slowly time varying electric and magnetic fields

Only a few epidemiological studies of groups with occupational exposures to static magnetic fields have been performed. Measurements of field levels are generally not available.

Time varying electromagnetic fields of frequencies of less than 100 kHz

Several epidemiological studies have reported an increased cancer incidence with children, adults and occupationally exposed workers associated with exposure to magnetic fields of 50 or 60 Hz. The reviews of the most important studies carried out by several national and international radiation protection bodies have resulted in similar conclusions. Available data do not provide convincing evidence of any cause-effect relationship between exposure and the development of cancer. They indicate, however, that the cancer risk associated with electromagnetic fields, if any, is very small. More data are needed to improve the epidemiological data base, and to test the biological plausibility of the hypothesised link between exposure to electromagnetic fields and cancer. The data related to cancer do not provide a basis for health risk assessment on human exposure to power frequency fields.

Electromagnetic fields and radiation of frequencies between 100 kHz and 300 GHz

Although the debate about possible health effects from exposure to electromagnetic fields in the last years has been mainly focused on extremely low frequency fields, a possible role of RF radiation in cancer promotion is now being investigated. As with extremely low frequency electromagnetic fields, the data related to RF fields and cancer while providing some support for an association between exposure and cancer do not provide convincing evidence of causality.

Optical radiation

A number of epidemiological studies have been carried out to investigate the association between exposure to solar radiation and skin cancer, including squamous and basal cell carcinoma and malignant melanoma. Reviews of these studies have been published by a number of different groups.

The evidence overall, both from descriptive and analytic epidemiology, strongly supports the notion that non-melanoma skin cancer aetiology is related to cumulative dose of solar radiation exposure. No competing hypothesis has been put forward which would satisfactorily explain the site distribution of these tumours, mainly on permanently exposed body sites, the increasing incidence with age, and the findings from person-based epidemiological studies. The findings from geographical studies, from the anatomical site distributions of the tumours, and from person-based epidemiology, suggest that squamous cell carcinoma (SCC) is more strongly related to UV exposure than is basal cell carcinoma (BCC). Data from patients treated with psoralen UVA (PUVA) show a strong dose-response relationship of the treatment to SCC risk and far less to BCC risk, although as yet the separate contributions of psoralen administration and UVA have not been established.

Incidence of cutaneous melanoma is increasing in white populations and the major risk factor appears to be exposure to solar radiation. While cumulative exposure to this factor is probably the main cause of melanomas of the head and neck, and there are insufficient data to assess the relationship of melanoma of unexposed sites to sun radiation exposure, intense short-term exposures of untanned skin appear likely to be the main cause of melanoma of intermittently exposed skin sites. There is no clear-cut evidence that use of sunlamps and sunbeds may be causative for melanoma, and more work is needed to clarify this. There is also evidence, particularly from data on migrants and recall of sunburn history, that exposures in childhood and adolescence may be of special importance to the risk of melanoma. Several of the results on this issue, however, are potentially biased, and therefore the relationship is still uncertain.

Overall, the data for cataract suggest, although with less certainty than for non-melanoma skin cancer, that cumulative UVR exposure is important to the aetiology of at least cortical cataracts.

It is unclear to what extent UV radiation is an important risk factor for cataracts in the general population in industrialised countries.

5   Hazard assessment

Static and slowly time varying electric and magnetic fields

Static electric fields act on the surface of the body. This may be accompanied by hair movement and other sensory stimulation in fields greater than 10 kV m^{-1}.

Static electric fields induce surface charges on conducting objects. Currents may pass through grounded people in contact with such objects. Field strengths greater than approximately 5 to 7 kV m^{-1} produce a wide variety of hazards associated with spark discharges and contact currents from ungrounded conductors within the field.

Concerning static magnetic fields, current scientific knowledge does not suggest any detrimental effect on major development, behavioural and physiological parameters for transient exposures to fields up to 2 T. From the established mechanisms of interaction, long-term exposure to static magnetic fields up to 200 mT should not have adverse consequences on health.

However, indirect field coupling may be more important than direct field coupling. For people with cardiac pacemakers, ferromagnetic implants, and implanted electronic devices, there are health risks if the magnetic flux density exceeds several mT. The majority of cardiac pacemakers are unlikely to be affected in fields less than 0.5 mT. There are also other vital electronic aids in increasing use that may be susceptible to static magnetic flux densities above a few mT particularly if the person is moving within the field.

Time varying electromagnetic fields of frequencies less than 100 kHz

For time varying electric fields, indirect field coupling may be more important than direct field coupling. Around 90% of exposed people have detection thresholds of greater than 10 to 15 kV m^{-1} due to sensations from hair vibration or tingling between body and clothes. Although these effects are not considered to be a hazard, they can become an annoyance.

Thresholds for perception or pain due to contact currents or spark discharges are relatively low and are dependent on the frequency and field strength, the size of the object and on the person's impedance to ground.

Examples are 2 to 2.5 kV m^{-1} for the median touch perception for children (finger contact with a car) and 8 to 10 kV m^{-1} for a painful shock for children (finger contact with a truck). The threshold for the perception of spark discharges by 10% of a group of volunteers close to an earthed object has been reported to be 0.6 to 1.5 kV m^{-1} at 50/60 Hz, with a similarly defined threshold for annoyance of 2 to 3.5 kV m^{-1}. Concerning time varying magnetic fields, health risk assessment is based on induced electric fields and currents in the body. From current scientific knowledge it may be concluded that functions of the central nervous system may be adversely affected by current densities above 10 mA m^{-2} between 10 Hz and 1 kHz and by progressively larger current densities at frequencies above and below this frequency range.

Several laboratory studies have been conducted on people exposed to 50/60 Hz magnetic fields. None of these investigations has revealed adverse clinical or significant physiological changes. The strongest magnetic flux density used was a 5 mT, 50 Hz field to which subjects were exposed for 4 h.

The lowest sensitivity thresholds for retinal visual stimulation (magnetophosphenes) are about 2 mT at 20 Hz and about 5 mT at 50 Hz.

The threshold value for a malfunction of some sensitive unipolar cardiac pacemakers is 20 μT (50 Hz) under worst case conditions. At about 200 μT most implanted pacemakers are influenced by 50 Hz magnetic fields.

Some epidemiological reports present data indicative of an increase in the incidence of cancer among children, adults, and occupational groups. These association cannot be satisfactorily explained by the available theoretical basis for the interaction of 50/60 Hz electromagnetic fields with living systems. The epidemiological studies have been reviewed and evaluated by several national and international radiation protection bodies. The conclusions of different expert groups are similar: although the more recent data reflect some improvements in methodology in laboratory studies and in epidemiological studies, the data related to cancer do not provide a basis for health risk assessment of human exposure to power frequency magnetic fields.

Electromagnetic fields and radiation of frequencies between 100 kHz and 300 GHz

Several factors need to be considered in the health assessment of exposure to radiofrequency radiation including: heating caused by the absorption of RF energy, the induction of currents in people by physical contact with metallic objects, and the absorption of RF energy in the form of pulsed fields. Here the peak power densities in the pulse should be considered separately from the average. Auditory perception is an example of a pulsed RF field effect.

Limited experimental evidence and theoretical calculations suggest that exposure of healthy resting people in moderate environmental conditions at whole body SARs in the range 1 to 4 W kg^{-1} for 30 minutes results in body temperature increases of less than 1°C. In addition, a review of the animal data indicates a threshold for behavioural responses in the same 1 to 4 W kg^{-1} range.

Higher energy absorption rates in extremities and limited body regions, do not appear to cause adverse effects, for SAR values below thresholds that are dependent on the body part and the volume.

In infants, the frail elderly, and in individuals taking certain drugs, thermoregulatory capacity may be reduced and, as a result, tolerance for the combined effects of RF exposure, exercise, solar radiation, and high ambient temperature, may be lower.

Superficial and deep burns may occur as a result of contact with metallic objects exposed to RF fields over a wide frequency range. Sufficiently high current densities for contact burns can be attained in RF fields that are too low to cause direct heating or stimulation. Thresholds depend on the size and shape of the object in contact with the body, field frequency, duration and type of contact, and other parameters.

At frequencies below approximately 1 MHz, interactions of RF fields with biological systems and potential hazards can be considered in terms of induced currents and current densities.

The use of induced current densities is only appropriate for the assessment of acute, immediate effects. The wave form of the RF field is an important factor to be considered in the response of biological systems.

Experimental data suggest that thresholds for the biological effects of absorbed energy at frequencies above hundreds of MHz, when in the form of short duration pulses (a few tens of μs), are lower than those for continuous fields at the same average energy level and the same SAR. This indicates that the peak value of energy transfer to the biological object can be an important determinant of the biological effect. A well-investigated effect is the perception of pulsed fields, such as from radar, as an audible sound described as a click, chirp, or knocking sensation.

There have been isolated reports that, in certain cell lines and in intact animals, RF exposure has been associated with increased growth rates of cells and tumours and with increases in the incidence of neoplastic transformations. Very few epidemiological studies have been reported.

The available evidence does not confirm that RF exposure results in the induction of cancer, or causes existing cancers to progress more rapidly. Because of incompleteness and inconsistencies, the available scientific evidence on carcinogenesis is an inadequate basis for recommendations of health protection guidelines.

Interference with the normal operation of electronic devices can arise due to exposure to RF fields. An important example of this related to human health is the observed interference of the emissions from certain cellular phones with the normal function of implanted pacemakers.

Optical radiation

Data on visible and IRR emissions for hazard analysis are limited.

With respect to the blue-light retinal hazard, assessments indicate that under normal usage there is no significant hazard associated with domestic room and street lighting. A potential hazard exists from viewing the sun directly, particularly with optical aids, and from prolonged direct viewing of certain lighting systems, although the luminances are sufficiently high that comfortable viewing of such sources for prolonged periods is unlikely and the aversion responses of the eye would be activated.

The main source of UVR with respect to public exposure is the sun and individual habits with respect to solar UVR exposure are important in assessing personal risk. Other sources for which published data exist for health hazard assessment are limited but include lighting systems (in the home and public places), medical sources (in hospitals and dentists surgeries) and welding arcs.

Data on emissions from laser sources for hazard analysis are generally more substantial than for non-laser sources. However, with lasers being increasingly used in many public areas, such as entertainment and display, hazardous exposure of the general public is possible.

6   National and international standards of protection against electromagnetic fields and radiation

Few countries in the European Union (EU) have promulgated standards for the protection of the general public against electromagnetic radiation. Austria, Germany and the United Kingdom have recommendations both for low and high frequency electromagnetic fields. In Italy, a law setting limits for exposure to 50 Hz electric and magnetic fields exists, whereas in Belgium the only existing regulation concerns fields generated by power lines.

The International Commission on Non-Ionizing Radiation Protection (ICNIRP) and its predecessor the International Non-Ionizing Radiation Committee of the International Radiation Protection Association (INIRC/IRPA) has produced guidelines on limits of exposure to static magnetic fields, 50/60 Hz electric and magnetic fields and radiofrequency radiation in the frequency range 100 kHz to 300 GHz.

The European Committee for Electrical Standardisation (CENELEC) has produced two pre-standards on human exposure to electromagnetic fields.

The adopted rationale within different countries and international standards is similar. There are some differences in methodological approach to protection. ICNIRP makes a general distinction between workers and members of the general public in setting limits. In Germany, a law setting limits for the general public is in preparation. Exposure limits for the general public are recommended by the "Strahlenschutzkommission (SSK)". In addition, standardisation committees have published national pre-standards. In the UK, field and contact current investigation levels are set as a practical aid to investigate compliance with restrictions.

7   Recommendations

Biological research

Electromagnetic fields of frequencies less than 100 kHz

- Central nervous system responses to induced electric current should be further investigated including, for example, further volunteer studies of deficits induced in tests of visual processing, reasoning and memory and *in vitro* brain slice studies of weak electric current effects.

- The possible increased susceptibility of some people to induced current, for example, those taking psychoactive drugs, epileptics etc., should be investigated. Such studies should be accompanied by appropriate dosimetric calculations.

- There is a particular need to coordinate studies of the possible carcinogenicity of electromagnetic fields, particularly at 50 Hz, within the EU. The experimental work should include co-carcinogenesis experiments, particularly looking at co-promotion in animal and cellular models, studies of effects on cell signalling and proliferation, particularly Ca^{2+} uptake and gene expression, and further study of effects on melatonin and its possible role in the suppression of mammary tumour growth.

- Further investigations of possible weak field interaction mechanisms particularly of experimentally testable hypotheses such as magnetic field effects on radical pair interactions have merit. Further study of weak electromagnetic field interactions with the optical system, in relation to effects on the production of melatonin by the pineal gland, should also be carried out.

Electromagnetic fields and radiation of frequencies between 100 kHz and 300 GHz

- There is further scope for the quantification of individual responses to whole body SARs. This would be particularly valuable in identifying the variation in individual susceptibilities within a population. In particular, magnetic resonance imaging (MRI) centres, which process large numbers of patients, should be encouraged to record and publish data relating to whole-body responses to SAR. Data from experimental volunteer studies examining thermoregulatory responses to radiofrequency exposure combined with adverse environmental conditions and various rates of physical exercise would also be useful in this regard.

- Human auditory and other responses to pulsed microwave and modulated RF radiation should be further investigated.

- Few studies have examined the possible carcinogenicity of RF and microwave radiation. In view of the increasing use of various RF or microwave emitting devices there is scope for a modest, coordinated programme of investigation of the possible carcinogenic effects at appropriate frequencies.

Optical radiation

- The implementation of test procedures to identify drugs, cosmetic and other substances that sensitise people to the effects of UVR should be supported.

- Studies on photobiological mechanisms of UVR-induced immune suppression should be supported.

- Studies on photobiological mechanisms of UVR-induced skin aging and UVR-induced degenerative effects on the ocular media should be supported.

- Basic biological research on skin cancer, particularly malignant melanoma, should be supported.

Epidemiological research
Electromagnetic fields and radiation
- Further efforts are clearly needed to determine whether exposure to magnetic fields or other factors in the residential environment may influence the risk of childhood cancer.
- There is an urgent need for large and statistically robust epidemiological studies based on objective measurements of exposure to electromagnetic fields. The feasibility of European-wide studies should be considered.

Optical radiation
- Epidemiological research on skin cancer, particularly malignant melanoma, should be supported.
- Research is needed on the relationship with UVR exposure, specially in childhood, to numbers of, and presence of, abnormal types of naevi.
- Research is required into the relation of exposure to artificial sources of UVR, including sunbeds, to risks of malignant melanoma and non melanoma skin cancers.
- Epidemiological studies on UVR-induced degenerative effects on the ocular media, particularly cataract, should be supported.
- The possibility of European-wide studies should be considered.

Exposure and dosimetry
Electromagnetic fields and radiation
- There is a need to be aware of the development of new technologies and the introduction of novel devices into the public domain which may materially affect the nature and the extent to which people may be exposed.
- Sources identified should be characterised in sufficient detail to enable exposure assessments to be carried out with respect to fundamental quantities restricting exposure. It should be recognised that spot environmental measurements may not completely characterise exposure in situations where the fields may be non-uniform and only partial body exposures arise.
- There is a need to further develop theoretical (computational) dosimetry based on anatomically and electrically realistic computational phantoms of the human body. This should be applied to determining internal fields and SARs resulting from exposure to external electric and magnetic fields and radiation.
- Support should be given to the dosimetric (computational and experimental) evaluation of SAR and temperature distribution within the body following localised or whole-body exposure.
- The use of personal exposure meters at 50 Hz power frequency should be encouraged to provide further information on the time distribution and magnitude of exposures. Such studies will enable specific sources contributing significantly to exposure to be identified and permit resources to be appropriately focused.
- There is a need for more information on the electromagnetic interference aspects of exposure to electric and magnetic fields.

- Information for the general public about levels of exposure to electromagnetic fields and human health should be developed and made available within the EU.

Optical radiation

- A coordinated measurement network to assess environmental levels of solar UVR across Europe should be established to obtain reliable measurement data relating to the major source of public exposure from optical radiation.

- Support should be given to the dosimetric evaluation of personal exposure from solar UVR and in particular the distribution across the body for a variety of pursuits.

- More reliable data on the UVR, visible and IRR emissions of a wider range of artificial optical sources for hazard analysis need to be obtained, as much of the existing data stems from occupational exposure conditions in the 1970s-1980s, and both the range of sources and exposure conditions are likely to have changed.

- With particular reference to UVR, more measurement information for health hazard assessment is required for sunbeds and solaria.

- With particular reference to light and IRR, more measurement information for health hazard assessment is required for common sources.

- With the development of laser technology, more measurement information for health hazard assessment is required for lasers used in the public domain and particularly for display and other entertainment lasers.

- The use of sunbeds should be discouraged as part of a public health awareness/education programme about UVR.

- Information for the general public and particularly for the carers of children about the hazards of overexposure to UVR should be developed and made available within the EU.

Standards development

- It is important that biological, epidemiological and dosimetric research relevant to the health effects of non-ionising radiation exposure is continuously reviewed by international and national bodies with responsibilities in radiation protection. Based on the results, guidance and limits of exposure should be revised if necessary. Scientific bodies should continue to rely only on scientific data relating to well-established health effects of non-ionising radiation.

- The development of health policies related to reducing the risks of exposure to non-ionising radiation will include decisions on political, economic and social aspects as well as on the scientific aspects. Within the EU, it would be preferable for such policies to be based on a wider international consensus.

1   Introduction

The objective of this report is to provide information about exposure of the general public from non-ionising radiation and about related health effects.

The report was commissioned and partly funded by Directorate General V of the European Commission and was produced collaboratively by a working group comprising staff from the National Radiological Protection Board (NRPB), United Kingdom; the Bundesamt für Strahlenschutz (BfS), Germany and the Istituto Superiore di Sanità (ISS), Italy. The conclusions and views expressed in this report do not necessarily reflect the official policies of the organisations concerned.

For the purpose of this document, the non-ionising radiation spectrum has been divided into the following areas; static and slowly time varying (frequencies less than a few Hz) electric and magnetic fields; time varying electric and magnetic fields of frequencies less than 100 kHz; time varying electromagnetic fields and radiation of frequencies between 100 kHz and 300 GHz; infrared and visible radiation; ultraviolet radiation and laser radiation, figure 1.1.

The physical characteristics of electromagnetic radiation and relevant measurement and dosimetric quantities and units are described in chapter 2.

Sources of non-ionising radiation to which members of the general public might be exposed or which might be present in areas to which the general public have access are described in chapter 3 together with data on possible exposure levels.

The biological effects of non-ionising radiation are described in chapter 4. The biological evidence relating to the possible carcinogenic effects of electromagnetic fields is summarised in this chapter.

Epidemiological studies play an important role in understanding the potential adverse effects of exposure to non-ionising radiation on human health and these are summarised in chapter 5.

The extent to which exposure to non-ionising radiation is likely to present a hazard to members of the general population is summarised in chapter 6. Here the emphasis is on the levels of non-ionising radiation to which the general public could be exposed in relation to well established biological effects and to maximum levels of exposure advised by radiation protection bodies.

International and national bodies with responsibilities for radiation protection have promulgated exposure guidelines and statutes containing recommended limits of exposure for non-ionising radiation. A summary of those guidelines relevant to the member states of the EU is presented in chapter 7.

Chapter 8 contains recommendations for further investigations.

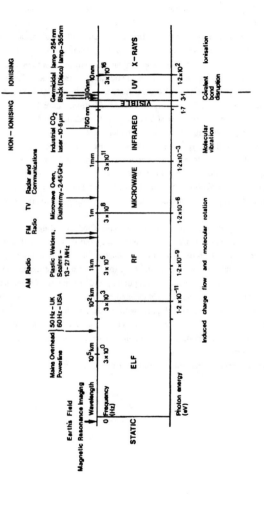

FIGURE 1.1 Non-ionising radiation spectrum

18

2 Physical interaction of non-ionising electromagnetic radiation with people

2.1 Static and slowly time varying fields

2.1.1 Electric fields

Electric charges exert forces on each other. It is convenient to introduce the concept of an electric field to describe this interaction. Thus, a system of electric charges produces an electric field at all points in space and any charge placed in the field will experience a force because of its presence. The electric field is denoted by E and is a vector quantity, which means that it has both magnitude and direction. The force F exerted on a point (infinitesimally small body) containing a net positive charge q placed in an electric field E is given by:

$$F = qE \qquad 2.1$$

In practice, the unit of electric field strength is the volt per metre ($V\ m^{-1}$).

An electric charge will be induced on the surface of an object within a static electric field. The consequence of this is that the electric field at the surface of an object, particularly where there is a small radius, such as at a point, can be larger than the unperturbed electric field (the field without the object present), although the field inside the object may be very small or zero. Electric fields are experienced as a force by electrically charged objects; for example, a force will be exerted on body hair, which may be perceived.

2.1.2 Magnetic fields

The fundamental vector quantities describing a magnetic field are the magnetic field strength H and the magnetic flux density B (also called the magnetic induction).

Magnetic fields, like electric fields, are produced by electric charges, but only when these charges are in motion. Magnetic fields exert forces on charges but, again, only on charges that are in motion.

The magnitude of the force F acting on an electric charge q moving with a velocity v in the direction perpendicular to a magnetic field of magnetic flux density B is given by:

$$F = qvB \qquad 2.2$$

where the direction of F is perpendicular to both those of v and B.

The unit of magnetic flux density is the tesla (T).

The magnetic field strength H is the force with which the field acts on an element of current situated at a particular point. The value of H is measured in the unit ampere per metre ($A\ m^{-1}$).

The magnetic flux density B rather than the magnetic field strength H (where $B = \mu H$), is used to describe the magnetic field generated by currents that flow in conductors. The value of μ (the magnetic permeability) is determined by the properties of the medium.

For most biological materials, the permeability μ is equal to μ_0, the value of permeability ($1.257\ 10^{-6}\ H\ m^{-1}$) of free space (air). Thus, for biological materials, the values of B and H are related by the constant μ_0.

The body is relatively "transparent" to magnetic fields; such fields will interact directly with magnetically anisotropic (or polarised) materials and moving charges.

Magnetic fields can alter nuclear and electron energy levels and spin orientation, and will exert a force on biological molecules (Tenforde 1985). Some of these interactions are exploited in the study of biological systems, for example in studies of biochemical reactions using nuclear magnetic resonance or electron spin resonance techniques. Magnetic field interactions with atomic nuclei are very weak compared with those with electrons and are likely to be of little biological consequence.

Biologically significant interactions with electrons will be those in which the magnetic field is able to alter unpaired electron spin orientation and affect the radical recombination rate. This effect has been well established in organic chemical reactions but has not been demonstrated unequivocally in biological systems.

As a result of the Lorentz forces exerted on moving charge carriers, static magnetic fields interact with ionic currents, to produce electric fields. In particular, flow potentials are generated across blood vessels by the flow of blood in a static field. Estimated maximum potentials generated across the human aorta range from about 7 to 16 mV T^{-1}.

A static magnetic field also exerts a physical force on a flowing conductor, such as blood, which is proportional to the ionic conduction current and the magnetic flux density. It has been predicted that the net effect of this magnetohydrodynamic interaction will be a drop in aortic blood flow rate of up to 7% in humans in a 5 T field (UNEP/WHO/IRPA 1987).

2.2   Time varying electromagnetic fields of frequencies less than 100 kHz

2.2.1   Electric fields

Since electric fields exert forces on charged particles, in an electrically conductive material, such as living tissue, these forces will set charges into motion to cause an electric current to flow. This current is frequently specified by the current density J the magnitude of which is equal to the current flowing through a unit surface perpendicular to its direction. The unit of current density is ampere per square metre (A m^{-2}). J is directly proportional to E in a wide variety of materials. Thus:

$$J = \sigma E \qquad\qquad 2.3$$

where the constant of proportionality σ is called the electrical conductivity of the medium. The unit of σ is siemens per metre (S m^{-1}).

Time varying electric fields induce surface charges on an exposed body which result in currents inside the body, the magnitudes of which are related to the surface charge density. Depending on the exposure conditions, size, shape, and position of the exposed body in the field, the surface charge density can vary greatly resulting in a variable and non-uniform distribution of currents inside the body. For sinusoidal electric fields the magnitude of the currents inside the body increases proportionally with frequency. For 50 Hz fields the internal electric field is less than about 10^{-6} to 10^{-7} of the field outside the body. The induced current density distribution varies inversely with the body cross-section and may be relatively high in the neck and ankles of people (Tenforde and Kaune 1987), table 2.1.

Besides direct coupling between the body and time varying electric fields, indirect coupling mechanisms are important when the exposed person is in the vicinity of other people or objects. The following indirect coupling mechanisms are of importance (UNEP/WHO/IRPA 1993).

- Electric charges induced in a conducting object (for example, an automobile) exposed to a time-varying electric field may cause a current to pass through a person in contact with it.

- Transient discharges (often called microshocks) can occur when people and metal objects exposed to a strong electric field come into sufficiently close proximity.

- Electric fields may interfere with implanted medical devices (for example, unipolar cardiac pacemakers) and cause malfunction.

2.2.2 Magnetic fields

Time varying magnetic fields act on people by inducing electric fields and currents inside the body.

Internal tissue current density J correlates with the external magnetic induction B according to Faraday's law:

$$ J = \frac{1}{2} R \sigma \frac{dB}{dt} \qquad 2.4 $$

for magnetic fields with a rate of change of magnetic flux density, dB/dt; for sinusoidal fields the amplitude of J reduces to $\pi R \sigma f B_o$ (R is the radius of inductive current loop (m), σ is the tissue conductivity (S m^{-1}), f is frequency (Hz) and B_o is the magnetic flux density amplitude (T)).

Consequently, the current density increases with frequency and magnetic flux density amplitude in addition to tissue conductivity and inductive loop radius. The appropriate inductive loop radius depends on the orientation of the magnetic field relative to the body. Theoretically, the largest current densities will be induced in the peripheral tissues and will decrease linearly towards the centre of the body as the inductive loop radius decreases. In practice, the calculation of current densities is complicated in that the exact current paths depend on the distribution of the conductive properties of body tissues.

Examples of 50 Hz electric current densities induced by magnetic fields are presented in table 2.1.

Besides these direct coupling mechanisms, magnetic fields coupling to a conductor (for example, a wire fence) cause electric currents to pass through the body of a person in contact with it.

Magnetic fields may interfere with implanted medical devices and cause malfunction.

2.3 Electromagnetic fields and radiation of frequencies between 100 kHz and 300 GHz

Electromagnetic fields and waves of frequencies between 100 kHz and 300 GHz are included in the radiofrequency (RF) portion of the electromagnetic spectrum. The frequency range between 300 MHz and 300 GHz is usually termed microwaves (MW).

TABLE 2.1 Induced current density ranges at 50 Hz (ILO 1994, after Tenforde and Kaune 1987)

Electric field strength (kV m^{-1})[a]				
Current density (mA m^{-2})	Trunk (average)	Head	Neck	Ankles, when both feet are grounded
10-100	30–300	100–1000	20–200	5–50
1-10	3–30	10–100	2–20	0.5–5
< 1	< 3	< 10	< 2	< 0.5

Magnetic flux density (mT)[b]			
Current density (mA m^{-2})	Trunk (R = 0.3 m)	Head (R = 0.075 m)	Wrist/ankles (R = 0.03 m)
10-100	0.6-6	2.5-25	6-60
1-10	0.06-0.6	0.25-2.5	0.6-6
< 1	< 0.06	< 0.25	< 0.6

(a)   Values of the electric field strength for approximately producing these current densities in different body parts.

(b)   Values of the magnetic flux density for approximately inducing these current densities in peripheral regions of different body parts (a homogeneous conductivity of 0.25 S m^{-1} is assumed).

When the frequency f of the source charges or currents is high enough, the electric and magnetic fields produced by sources will radiate from them. A convenient and commonly used description of this radiation is wave propagation. The basic ideas of wave propagation are illustrated in figure 2.1. The distance from one ascending, or descending, node to the next is defined as the wavelength, and is usually denoted by λ. The speed of propagation is the speed at which the wave is travelling and is equal to the distance travelled divided by the time taken.

The quantities frequency and wavelength are related by the equation: $\lambda = v/f$, where v is the speed of light in the traversed medium. The wavelength becomes much shorter in biological media, especially those containing a large proportion of water.

A plane wave is a model that approximately represents some electromagnetic waves. Its defining characteristics are:

- The wave fronts are planes (spheres with very small curvature).

- E, H, and the direction of propagation are all mutually perpendicular.

- E/H is called the wave impedance. For free space, E/H = 377 ohms (Ω).

- Power density, S, is the power per unit area normal to the direction of propagation, and is expressed in the unit watt per square metre (W m^{-2}): $S = E^2/377 = 377H^2 = EH$.

- Both E and H vary as 1/r, where r is the distance from the source.

22

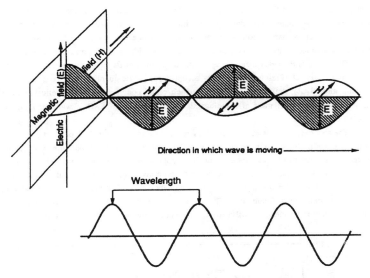

FIGURE 2.1 Electromagnetic monochromatic wave. Electromagnetic waves consist of a moving pattern of electric and magnetic fields whose direction of propagation is perpendicular to the directions of oscillations of the fields. The distance between successive crests or troughs of the wave is the wavelength. (courtesy of ICNIRP)

The region close to a source is called the near-field. Here the electric and magnetic fields are not necessarily perpendicular, and are not always conveniently characterised by waves. They are often non-propagating in nature and are called fringing fields or induction fields. The near-fields often vary rapidly with distance and mathematical expressions denoting their magnitude with distance from the source generally contain the terms $1/r$, $1/r^2$, $1/r^3$,..., where r is the distance from the source to the point at which the field is being determined.

At greater distances from the source, the $1/r^2$, $1/r^3$, and higher-order terms are negligible compared with the $1/r$ term in the field variation, and the fields are called far-fields (plane waves). Depending very much on the application, RF power may be generated as a continuous wave (CW) at essentially a single frequency, or it may be amplitude, frequency, or pulse modulated (AM, FM, and PM).

Radiofrequency energy is reflected, refracted, diffracted, scattered and absorbed, and the same general principles apply as with all electromagnetic radiation. However, because of the wavelengths involved, reflection or scattering can significantly increase local field strength due to standing waves or multipath interference.

Electric and magnetic fields interact with materials in two ways. First, the electric and magnetic fields exert forces on the charged particles in the materials, thus altering the charge patterns that originally existed. Second, the altered charge patterns in the materials produce additional electric and magnetic fields (in addition to the fields that were originally applied). In non-magnetic materials, mainly the applied electric field has an effect on the charges in the material. This occurs in three primary ways: polarisation of bound charges, orientation of permanent dipoles, and drift of conduction charges (both electronic and ionic). Materials primarily affected by the first two effects are called dielectrics; materials primarily affected by the third one, conductors.

Dosimetry is the assessment of the spatial distribution of RF energy or power deposition in an irradiated subject. Presently, the widely accepted dosimetric quantity is the specific energy absorption rate (SAR), defined as the rate at which radiofrequency electromagnetic energy is imparted to an element of mass of a biological body. The unit of SAR is watt per kilogram (W kg^{-1}).

The absorption and distribution of RF energy in the body are strongly dependent on the size and orientation of the body and the frequency and polarisation of the incident radiation. Both theory and experiment show that RF absorption in the body approaches a maximum value when the long axis of the body is both parallel to the electric field vector and approximately equal to four-tenths of the wavelength of the incident RF field. This frequency-dependent behaviour is illustrated in figure 2.2 for people of different size. The average whole-body SAR in W kg^{-1} is plotted as a function of radiation frequency in MHz for an incident average power density of 1 W m^{-2}.

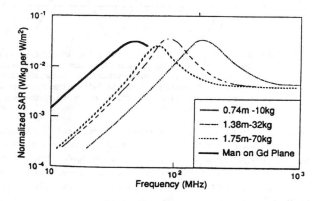

FIGURE 2.2   **The specific absorption rate (SAR) in W kg^{-1} per unit incident power density in W m^{-2} for people of different size (courtesy of ICNIRP)**

Based on the absorption characteristics in the human body, the radiofrequency range can be subdivided into four regions.

- The sub-resonance range, less than about 30 MHz where energy absorption increases rapidly with frequency.

- The resonance range, which extends from about 30 MHz to about 300 MHz for the whole body, and to greater frequencies if partial body resonances are considered.

- The range, extending from about 400 MHz up to about 2 GHz or so, where significant localized energy absorption can be expected. Energy absorption decreases when frequency increases due to changing penetration depth with frequency from several cm at about 900 MHz to about one cm at 3 GHz.

- The surface absorption range, greater than about 10 GHz or so, where absorption becomes increasingly superficial and the temperature elevation is localised at the surface of the body.

2.4   Optical radiation

Optical radiation comprises ultraviolet radiation (UVR), visible radiation and infrared radiation (IRR) and is the part of the electromagnetic spectrum covering the wavelength range 10 nm to 1 mm (Sliney and Wolbarsht 1980, McKinlay *et al* 1988). Radiation of wavelengths less than 180 nm is strongly absorbed in air and therefore does not represent any direct radiation hazard. However, the production of toxic ozone can result as an indirect hazard from absorption processes in air at wavelengths principally below about 240 nm. The natural (solar) optical spectrum at the Earth's surface extends from about 290 nm to 1 mm. Radiation of wavelengths less than about 290 nm is absorbed in the Earth's atmosphere.

Optical radiation is produced principally by the excitation and subsequent de-excitation of atoms and molecules. In this way, an electron in a stable orbit around the nucleus of an atom is excited into a higher energy orbit by an interaction (eg, collision) process involving an energy exchange and subsequently returns to its original state, losing its energy as radiation. A less common means of production occurs in high energy physics research whereby optical radiation results from the acceleration of charged particles (synchrotron radiation).

Optical radiation can also be produced by the vibration and rotation of atoms and molecules within a material. It is emitted from physical matter in accordance with the laws of black body radiation taking into account its emissivity (ie, the ratio of the total energy emitted per unit surface area at a specific absolute temperature T to that of a black body). Many emitters produce radiation with a continuum of wavelengths with the wavelength (expressed in μm) of maximum spectral power denoted by 2898/T. As the temperature of the emitter increases, both the total power and the peak spectral power increase with the latter moving to shorter wavelengths, figure 2.3.

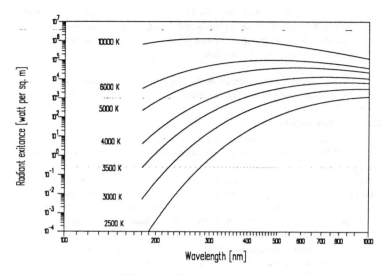

FIGURE 2.3   Spectral emissions from black body radiators at different temperatures. (McKinlay 1992)

In considering direct radiation hazards, the UVR spectrum extends from 180 to 400 nm and consists of three main regions: UVC (100 to 280 nm), UVB (280 to 315 nm) and UVA (315 nm to 400 nm) (CIE 1987). The visible spectrum extends from 400 to 780 nm. The peak wavelengths for visual responses are 507 nm (scotopic (night) vision) and 555 nm (photopic (day) vision). The IRR spectrum extends from 780 nm to 1 mm and consists of three regions: IRA (780 to 1400 nm), IRB (1400 to 3000 nm) and IRC (3000 nm to 1 mm) (CIE 1987), table ES.2. Radiation in each of the defined spectral regions interacts with different biological targets and has different interaction mechanisms and ranges of penetration. However, the effects can overlap wavelength ranges.

The quantity and spatial and temporal distribution of optical radiation are described in terms of the so-called radiometric quantities and units. These quantities are physically absolute in the sense that they do not depend on the spectral (wavelength) response of a receptor or detector.

Laser is an acronym for light amplification by stimulated emission of radiation. It is applied to devices that emit intense, coherent, directional beams of optical radiation. The basic laser process involves an electron or molecule undergoing a stimulated quantum jump from a higher to a lower energy state, causing a spatially and temporally coherent beam of optical radiation to be emitted. In general, a laser consists of an active medium in a resonant cavity and a source of excitation energy.   The active medium is excited to achieve laser action.   A pattern of electromagnetic waves builds up to a very high intensity in the resonant cavity by repeated reflections along the cavity from mirrored end-windows and radiates out through one of these windows which is less reflective.

Laser radiation is coherent, figure 2.4. The emitted photons are in-phase (temporally coherent) and appear to the eye to have been generated from a point source (spatially coherent) and therefore can be focused by simple lenses, for example the eye, to form a very small spot size.

They are also (generally) monochromatic, uni-directional and have the same polarisation. A laser beam has (generally) a low divergence (ie, it travels in near-parallel lines from its source). These combined properties can result in very high power densities in the beam. Various solids, liquids, gases and diode junctions can act as laser active media, allowing the achievement of stimulated emission at distinct wavelengths throughout the UVR, visible and IRR spectrum. Depending on the active medium and system design, the emission duration can vary from single pulses of duration less than 10^{-13} s to a continuous wave. Commonly used lasers emit power levels that range from a few μW to several kW and pulsed radiation can vary greatly in the duration, energy and repetition frequency of the pulses. Particular exceptions to monochromaticity are dye lasers and particular exceptions to highly collimated beams are semiconductor lasers and laser arrays.

Because of the great dependence of the type and magnitude of biological (including hazardous) effects on the wavelength of the radiation it is important to have information about the spectral emissions of such sources. For hazard analysis the most useful information is a set of data comprising spectral irradiance (W m^{-2} nm^{-1}) measurements of the source emissions at the target. The (total) irradiance (W m^{-2}) can be obtained by summing over all wavelengths of interest. The biologically effective (weighted) irradiance (W m^{-2} effective) for any specific biological (hazardous) effect is obtained by multiplying the spectral irradiance at each wavelength by a factor (biological or hazard weighting factor) that quantifies the relative efficacy of radiation of that wavelength for causing the effect. Such factors are obtained from action spectra (efficacy curves) based on experimentally obtained values for the quantity of radiation of each wavelength which will just cause the effect. In constructing action spectra in this way all the data are normalised to the datum at a chosen wavelength, usually at the most efficacious. By summing the calculated biologically effective irradiance over the exposure time the biologically weighted radiant exposure (J m^{-2} effective) is obtained. This quantity is often referred to as dose.

Visible radiation (light) interacts with the eye and produces the visual sensation. Like other components of the optical spectrum, light can interact with matter in various ways, such as absorption, refraction, reflection and scattering. Non-laser optical radiation sources generally produce divergent polychromatic beams with constantly changing phase relationships.

When optical radiation passes through a medium its propagation is affected in two respects. Its velocity is different in the medium from that in free space with respect to both direction and amplitude, and its intensity progressively decreases as it penetrates into the medium. Removal of radiant energy from the incident beam is achieved by absorption and scattering processes. The major physical interactions of optical radiation with biological tissues include specular and diffuse reflection, refraction, scattering and absorption. Energy must be absorbed to produce the physical and chemical changes that result in a biological effect. Photochemical effects (ie, chemical changes in target cells initiated, assisted or accelerated by exposure to optical radiation) are important in the UVR and shorter wavelength visible spectral regions. Thermal effects are dominant in the IRR and visible spectral regions.

2.5   Summary

2.5.1   Static and slowly time varying fields

Static electric fields induce electric charges on the surface of an object. These charges may cause forces on each other; for example, a force will be exerted on body hair, which may be perceived. Additionally, discharges can occur when people and metal objects come into close proximity.

Static magnetic fields interact with living matter through three established physical mechanisms: magnetic induction (electrodynamic interactions with moving electrolytes and Faraday currents), magnetomechanical effects (most important are force effects on ferromagnetic materials) and electronic interactions.

2.5.2   Time varying electromagnetic fields of frequencies less than 100 kHz

Since time dependent electric fields induce a surface charge on an exposed body, varying with frequency, this results in currents inside the body. For sinusoidal electric fields the magnitudes of the currents inside the body increase proportionally with frequency. Magnetic fields act on people by inducing electric fields and circulating currents inside the body. The current density increases with frequency and magnetic flux density amplitude, and also with tissue conductivity and inductive loop radius.

Beside the direct coupling mechanisms, indirect coupling mechanisms are of importance. Electric and magnetic field coupling to a conductor causes electric currents to pass through the body of a person in contact with it. Transient discharges (often called microshocks) can occur when people and metal objects exposed to a strong electric field come into sufficiently close proximity. Electric and magnetic fields may interfere with implanted medical devices and cause malfunction.

2.5.3   Electromagnetic fields and radiation of frequencies between 100 kHz and 300 GHz

When source charges or currents oscillate at frequencies in the radiofrequency and microwave range, electric and magnetic fields produced by these sources will radiate from them. A convenient and commonly used description of this radiation is wave propagation (far-field). The region close to a source is called the near-field. In this region the electric and magnetic fields are often non-propagating in nature and are sometimes referred to as fringing fields or reactive near-fields. In this case, objects located near sources may strongly affect the nature of the fields.

Radiofrequency and microwave fields and waves induce electric fields and corresponding electric currents in biological systems exposed to these fields. The intensities and spatial distribution of induced currents are dependent on various characteristics of the exposure field and geometry, and the exposed biological system (its size, shape, and electric properties). When interactions are due to the rate of energy deposition per unit mass, the dosimetric quantity specific energy absorption rate (SAR) is used, most often expressed in watts per kilogram.

Whole-body SAR is strongly dependent on frequency and the orientation of the electric field relative to the longest dimension of the body. The highest rate of energy deposition occurs for frequencies such that the major length of the irradiated body is approximately 0.36 to 0.40 times the free-space wavelength, λ, of radiation. For near-field exposure SARs considerably lower than those for far-field conditions are observed.

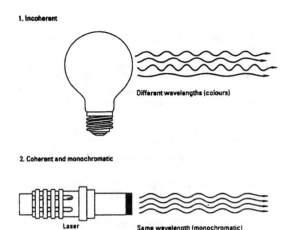

1. Incoherent

Different wavelengths (colours)

2. Coherent and monochromatic

Laser

Same wavelength (monochromatic)
Light waves in phase (coherent)

FIGURE 2.4 Laser radiation compared with optical radiation from a conventional light source. (courtesy of ICNIRP)

2.5.4 Optical radiation

Optical radiation comprises ultraviolet radiation (UVR), visible and infrared (IRR) radiations and is the part of the electromagnetic spectrum covering the wavelength range 10 or 100 nm to 1 mm.

It is produced principally by the excitation and subsequent de-excitation of atoms and molecules.

Optical radiation can also be produced by the vibration and rotation of atoms and molecules within a material. It is emitted from physical matter in accordance with the laws of black body radiation taking into account its emissivity.

When optical radiation passes through a medium its propagation is affected in two respects. Its velocity is different in the medium from that in free space and its intensity progressively decreases as it penetrates into the medium. Removal of radiant energy from the incident beam is achieved by absorption and scattering processes. The major physical interactions of optical radiation with biological tissues include specular and diffuse reflection, refraction, scattering and absorption.

Laser is an acronym for light amplification by stimulated emission of radiation. It is applied to devices that emit intense, coherent, directional beams of optical radiation.

Laser radiation is coherent. The emitted photons are in-phase (temporally coherent) and appear to the eye to have been generated from a point source (spatially coherent) and therefore can be focused by the eye to form a very small spot size. They are also (generally) monochromatic, uni-directional and have the same polarisation and velocity. A laser beam has (generally) a low divergence (ie, it travels in near-parallel lines from its source). These combined properties can result in very high power densities in the beam.

References

CIE. 1987. *International lighting vocabulary.* Vienna, International Commission on Illumination, Publication No 17.4.

ILO. 1994. Protection of workers from power frequency electric and magnetic fields. Occupational safety and health series No. 69. Geneva, International Labour Office.

McKinlay, A F. 1992. Artificial sources of UVA radiation: Uses and emission characteristics. IN *Biological Responses to Ultraviolet A Radiation* (Urbach, F, ed). Overland Park, Valdermar Publishing Company.

McKinlay, A F, Harlen, F, and Whillock, M J. 1988. *Hazards of Optical Radiation. A Guide to Sources, Uses and Safety.* Bristol and Philadelphia, Adam Hilger.

Sliney, D, and Wolbarsht, M. 1980. *Safety with Lasers and Other Optical Sources.* New York and London, Plenum Press.

Tenforde, T S. 1985. Mechanisms for biological effects of magnetic fields. IN *Biological Effects and Dosimetry of Static and ELF Electromagnetic Fields,* (Grandolfo, M, Michaelson, S M, and Rindi, A eds). New York, Plenum Press.

Tenforde, T S, and Kaune, W T. 1987. Interaction of extremely low frequency electric and magnetic fields with humans. *Health Phys.,* **53**, 595–606.

UNEP/WHO/IRPA. 1987. *Magnetic fields. Environmental Health Criteria 69.* Geneva, World Health Organization.

UNEP/WHO/IRPA. 1993. *Electromagnetic fields. Environmental Health Criteria 137 (300 Hz to 300 GHz).* Geneva, World Health Organization.

3 Sources and exposure

Sources of non-ionising radiation exposure can in principle be subdivided into those of artificial origin, that are produced by humans, and those having their origin in a natural process, for which meteorological phenomena almost exclusively play a role.

The natural electromagnetic environment originates from the properties of the Earth, from processes such as discharges in the Earth's atmosphere (terrestrial sources) or in the sun and in deep space (extraterrestrial sources).

With the advent of the technological age, the widespread use of electrical appliances, electromagnetic energy, high voltage power lines, medical diagnostic and therapeutic equipment, telecommunication, broadcast, radar, etc, has markedly increased environmental exposures to static and extremely low frequency (ELF) electromagnetic fields and to radiofrequency (including microwave) radiation.

Optical radiation from the sun is the most important source with respect to exposure of the general population. Artificial sources of optical radiation to which the public can be exposed are divided into two main categories: (a) non-coherent sources, such as fluorescent lamps and infrared heating elements, and (b) coherent (laser) sources, for example those incorporated into consumer products or used for entertainment or display.

3.1 Static and slowly time varying fields

3.1.1 Electric fields

Natural background

The electric fields of the Earth consist of a static component, which is dominant, and a time varying component, which is smaller by several orders of magnitude. The source of the static electric field is the spherical capacitor, which the Earth resembles. The lower troposphere is considered as the dielectric in this capacitor that is formed by the electrically conducting surface of the Earth and by the electrically conducting atmosphere above 40 km. This capacitor is being charged continuously by lightning discharges from thunderstorms all over the world. Due to the separation of electric charge between the atmosphere and the ground, the natural static electric field near the Earth's surface has a field strength of about 130 V m^{-1} (Dolezalek 1979). Daily changes in the natural electric field are attributed to factors, such as thunderstorms, that affect the rate of charge transfer between the ground and the upper atmosphere. Large field variations occur near thunderstorms, where electric fields of 3 to 20 kV m^{-1} have been observed. Even in the absence of local lightning, field strengths may reach 100 V m^{-1} to 3 kV m^{-1}. Large deviations from the fair-weather field, up to 200%, are also expected in the presence of fog or rain. The electric field varies also with height, local temperature, humidity profile and the presence of ionised contaminants.

Fields involved in normal biological functions

Static and ELF electric and magnetic fields, and their associated currents, play a very important role in many biological functions. There is a very intense (about 10^7 V m^{-1}) electric field located at the cell membrane due to the potential difference maintained between the inside and outside of the cell. Static potentials characterise the cell mass during early stages of embryonic growth, and are associated with the process of differentiation at its very beginning.

The dominant cause of static electric fields in the environment is charge separation as a result of motion. People walking on non-conductive carpets can be charged up to electric potentials of several kV. This may result in an electric field strength near the body of around 10 kV m^{-1} or so and sometimes as high as 500 kV m^{-1}. Handling and treating of plastic material result in large static electric fields up to several hundred kV m^{-1}. Close to visual display units (VDUs) significant static electric fields can be measured. Typical values at 30 cm distance are tens of kV m^{-1}.

Distribution of electric power

In some cases in Europe, electric power is supplied via high voltage DC transmission lines. Those lines operate at voltages up to about 500 kV. Fields of up to 20 kV m^{-1} can be measured directly under the conductor. These fields decrease only slowly with distance. At 400 m the field values are approximately 2 kV m^{-1} and at 800 m are up to 1 kV m^{-1}.

Transportation systems

Some public transportation systems use DC supplies. For example, underground systems or tramways operate at 600 V DC. The resulting fields at 5 m distance are around 30 V m^{-1}. In some European countries railways operate at 1.5, 3, or even 6 kV DC. This will cause electric fields of up to 300 V m^{-1} inside the train.

3.1.2   Magnetic fields

Natural background

The natural magnetic field is the sum of an internal field originating from the electric current flowing in the upper layer of the Earth's core and an external field generated in the environment from such factors as solar activity, atmospherics, etc. At the surface of the Earth, the vertical component is maximal at the magnetic poles, amounting to about 6.7 10^{-5} T (67 µT) and is zero at the magnetic equator. The horizontal component is maximal at the magnetic equator, about 3.3 10^{-5} T (33 µT), and is zero at the magnetic pole. The geomagnetic field exhibits temporal and spatial variations related predominantly to solar activity and local magnetic aberrations. Measurements carried out in the UK (Swanson 1994) showed local variations in homes of up to ± 10 µT from the unperturbed geomagnetic field (48 µT).

Workplace and home

Important new technologies may involve exposures to magnetic fields. One is the superconducting magnet energy storage ring where the magnetic flux density at the surface of the Earth, 600 m above the buried solenoid, is approximately 20 mT. The maximum magnetic flux densities in areas accessible to people are estimated to be between 20 and 50 mT.

In the home there are in general no sources of static magnetic fields relevant to human health. In some countries there is a sporadic individual use of magnetic plasters, blankets and mattresses, which are claimed to prevent non-specific diseases. Typical field strengths at the surface are about 50 mT with a very steep decrease within distances of a few millimetres or so. Headphones and telephone speakers may produce 0.3 to 1.0 mT directly at their surfaces. The static magnetic field components from battery powered devices are very small compared with the natural background and thus of minor importance.

Distribution of electric power

High voltage DC transmission lines usually produce only small magnetic fields of approximately tens of μT.

Transport systems

Tramways typically operate at approximately 500 A DC. The resulting magnetic fields inside are around 80 μT. Inside DC operated railways the static magnetic field can reach values of up to 2 mT. Measurements made inside high speed trains in Italy (30 kV DC) showed magnetic flux density values up to 1 mT at a maximum speed of 250 km h^{-1} (Grandolfo *et al* 1989). Modern magnetic levitation (maglev) systems use very high fields (around 1 T) directly on the rails. Depending on the technical design, inside the train there are stray fields between 50 μT and 10 mT.

3.2 Time varying electromagnetic fields of frequencies less than 100 kHz

The most important sources of human-made fields in the ELF range operate at the power frequencies of 50 or 60 Hz.

3.2.1 Electric fields

Natural background

Atmospheric fields of frequencies less than 30 MHz originate predominantly from thunderstorms and magnetic pulsations that produce currents within the Earth. Their field strengths and range of frequencies vary widely with geographical location, time of day and season. Local variations occur depending on atmospheric conditions and variations in the magnetic field. The geographical dependence is such that the highest levels are observed in equatorial areas and the lowest in polar areas. Overall, atmospheric fields have an emission spectrum with the largest amplitude components having frequencies of between 2 and 30 kHz. Generally, the atmospheric field level decreases with increasing frequency.

The natural electric field strength at the power frequencies of 50 or 60 Hz is about 10^{-4} V m^{-1}. In the frequency range 5 to 1000 Hz, field strengths of 10^{-4} to 0.5 V m^{-1} can be measured.

The main characteristics of the Earth's electric field are presented in table 3.1.

TABLE 3.1 Characteristics of the Earth's electric field in the ELF range

Frequency range (Hz)	Nature of the field	Field strength (V m^{-1})
0.001–5	Short duration pulses of magnetohydrodynamic origin	$0.2–10^3$
7.5–8.4 and 26–27	3–6 quasisinusoidal pulses of undetermined origin	$(0.15–0.6) 10^{-6}$
5–1000	Related to atmospheric changes (atmospherics)	$10^{-4}–0.5$

Workplace and home

The principal human-made sources of ELF electromagnetic fields are high voltage transmission lines, and all devices containing current carrying wires, including equipment and appliances in industry and in the home. Human-made fields are stronger than those of natural origin by many orders of magnitude. Environmental exposures are often categorised as acute or chronic. In the home people are chronically exposed to fields of at least a few V m^{-1}, and people spending much time near high voltage equipment or working for power companies maintaining such equipment may be acutely exposed for several days a week to fields of several kV m^{-1}.

In the home or workplace, ELF electric fields occur near electrical wiring, appliances and light fixtures, or industrial electrical machines. Measurements of the average electric field strength in a typical home in an industrialised country range from less than 1 to about 15 V m^{-1}. The electric field strength in homes shows a great local variability with highest values near the sources. Ambient electric fields in homes can reach peak values around 100 V m^{-1}. These fields are, however, very inhomogeneous. Typical field levels from 50/60 Hz electric sources are shown in table 3.2.

TABLE 3.2 Field levels from 50/60 Hz electric field sources (from UNEP/WHO/IRPA 1984, Grandolfo and Vecchia 1985, Bernhardt 1988, Allen 1991)

Electric field source	Electric field strength (kV m^{-1})
Earth	10^{-7}
Overhead transmission lines (Maximum field under line)	
110 kV	1–2
245 kV	2–3
380 kV	5–6
800 kV	10–12
Office and household levels	
30 cm from appliances	0.01–0.5
ambient, distant appliances	0.001–0.01
30 cm from VDUs, DC	0.1–30
ELF	0.030–1.5

Appliances produce electric fields depending on their design. Very high values can be measured close to some heating blankets (6 to 7 kV m^{-1}). Average blankets show values around 500 V m^{-1}. Electric fields near infrared lamps can be as high as 1 kV m^{-1}. Visual display units can cause power frequency fields up to 300 V m^{-1} with a broad spectrum up to 11 kHz. All appliances with electric motors produce such a broad spectrum, with an emission maximum near 10 to 20 kHz and field strength of the order of 20 V m^{-1}. Table 3.3 presents typical values of electric field strengths in the vicinity of various domestic electrical appliances.

TABLE 3.3 60 Hz electric fields measured at 30 cm from various domestic electrical appliances (Grandolfo et al 1985)

Appliance	Electric field strength (V m^{-1})
Incandescent light bulb	2
Electric range	4
Clock	15
Vacuum cleaner	16
Coffee pot	30
Colour TV	30
Hair dryer	40
Vaporiser	40
Toaster	40
Phonograph	40
Hand mixer	50
Iron	60
Refrigerator	60
Stereo	90
Broiler	130
Electric blanket	250

Distribution of electric power

High voltage (HV) lines are operated at several standard voltages ranging from 130 to 750 kV, and construction of lines up to 1.5 MV is in progress. Most widely used are alternating current (AC) three-phase HV lines. There are several primary influences on the electric field strength beneath an overhead transmission line. These include:

●   the height of the conductors above ground (which is influenced by the ambient temperature and heating caused by the current passing through the conductor);

●   the geometric configuration of conductors and earthing wires on the towers, and in the case of two circuits in proximity, the relative phase sequencing;

●   the proximity of the grounded metallic structure of the tower;

●   the proximity of other tall objects (trees, fences, etc);

●   the lateral distance from the centreline of the transmission line;

●   the height above ground at the point of measurement;

●   the actual (rather than the nominal) voltage on the line.

Inside buildings near HV transmission lines, electric field strengths are typically lower than the unperturbed field by a factor of about 10 to 100, depending on the structure of the building and the type of materials. At lateral distances of about twice the line height, electric field strength decreases with distance in an approximately linear fashion. Nominal maximum values of electric field strength of about 10 kV m^{-1} can exist beneath 765 kV lines at 1 m above ground. Reference to typical measured or calculated field contours in the vicinity of the line (Zaffanella and Deno 1978) indicates that, for a 525 kV transmission line (height about 10 m), the field strength is always less than 1 kV m^{-1} at distances of more than 40 m from the outer conductor, while for a 1050 kV line, which has much higher conductors, the 1 kV m^{-1} field strength level occurs at a distance of about 100 m from the outer conductor. Typically, where a right-of-way is used for a transmission line of 500 kV or more, it varies from 35 to 70 m, so that electric fields at the edge of the right-of-way are of the order of 1 kV m^{-1}.

Transport systems

Most of the lines of European railway systems are electrified, using a supply voltage between 10 and 30 kV and frequencies of 16⅔ Hz or 50 Hz. The resulting electric field strength inside the train is around 1 V m^{-1}. Outside the train, on the platform of a station, electric field strengths reach values around 10 V m^{-1} (Gourdon 1993).

3.2.2 Magnetic fields

Natural background

The external magnetic field consists of many components differing in spectral and energy characteristics (Polk, 1974). Variations in magnetic fields are related to solar activity, particularly with respect to the ELF components, which change over 11-year and 27-day periods and also exhibit circadian variations. Other causes of variation in natural magnetic fields are thunderstorms, atmospheric changes, and air ionisation. About 2000 thunderstorms occur simultaneously over the globe, and lightning strikes the Earth's surface between 100 and 200 times per second; the currents involved may reach 2 10^5 A at the level of the Earth. Resulting electromagnetic fields have a very broad frequency range (from a few Hz up to a few MHz), and propagate over long distances. The characteristics of the Earth's magnetic field can be summarised as follows:

- fields with amplitudes from 4 10^{-2} to 8 10^{-2} A m^{-1} at pulsation frequencies ranging from 0.002 to 0.1 Hz;

- geomagnetic pulsations up to 5 Hz are of short duration, lasting from a few minutes to a few hours;

- amplitudes of fields decrease with increasing frequency from 8 10^{-6} A m^{-1} at 5 to 7 Hz to 8 10^{-9} A m^{-1} at 3 kHz;

- at 50 or 60 Hz, the natural magnetic field is approximately 10^{-9} mT (Polk 1974).

The Schumann resonances are also a source of magnetic fields. They may be explained in terms of standing waves which exist in the Earth-ionosphere cavity as a result of the extremely low attenuation factor at ELF frequencies in air. A typical value of horizontal magnetic field strength per unit frequency bandwidth is 500 nA m^{-1} Hz$^{-1/2}$. The largest time-varying atmospheric magnetic fields arise intermittently from intense solar activity and thunderstorms, and reach intensities of about $5 \ 10^{-7}$ T during large magnetic storms.

The main characteristics of the Earth's magnetic field in the ELF range are summarised in table 3.4.

TABLE 3.4 Characteristics of the Earth's magnetic field in the ELF range

Nature and origin	Amplitude changes (A m^{-1})	Frequency (Hz)	Time
Regular 24 hours variation related to ionospheric currents due to solar or lunar influence	0.024–0.040 (solar) 0.004–0.005 (lunar) Increasing during summer and towards the equator	–	–
Irregular, magnetic storms related to solar flares	0.8–2.4	Wide range of frequencies	
Natural fluctuations (micropulsations) depending upon the conditions of ionosphere and magnetosphere	$8 \ 10^{-5}$–$4 \ 10^{-2}$	0.001–5	During the day for hours

Fields involved in normal biological function

The normal brain rhythms patterns are predominantly below 20 Hz, although fields at higher frequencies are present. The activity of the nervous system creates electrical signals which affect muscle or gland function. Magnetic flux densities from various biological sources span many orders of magnitude, from 1 nT in the lung to 20 fT associated with activity evoked in the brain. Such very small fields can be measured in the body and biophysical investigations aim to use the results for medical diagnosis.

Workplace and home

Time-varying electromagnetic fields originating from human-made sources generally have much higher intensities than naturally occurring fields. For the general public the dominant exposure is due to the distribution and the domestic use of electric power with frequencies of 50 or 60 Hz. Field levels are shown in table 3.5.

TABLE 3.5 Field levels from 50/60 Hz magnetic field sources (from Krause 1986, Stuchly 1986, Bernhardt 1988, Allen 1991)

Magnetic field source	Magnetic flux density	
	Average level (mT)	Peak level (mT)
Earth	10^{-9}	-
Overhead transmission lines (380 & 765 kV)	0.01–0.04	0.4 (during failure)
Overhead transmission line 380 kV, 25 m from midspan	0.008	-
Standard homes	10^{-5}–10^{-3}	10^{-3}–$4 \ 10^{-2}$
Home with electric heating	$1.2 \ 10^{-2}$	–
30 cm from domestic appliances	-	10^{-2}–1
30 cm from VDUs	$8 \ 10^{-4}$	0.005–0.018
Medicine		
Therapeutic equipment	1–16	-

Most of the other common sources of electromagnetic fields are relatively small and low powered. For appliances that produce magnetic flux densities up to a few mT at a distance of 3 cm, the decline of the field strength at 30 cm may be more than a factor of 100 depending on the structure of the source. Depending on proximity to appliances, typical values for ambient 50/60 Hz magnetic flux density range from about 100 nT to about 1 mT. Table 3.6 presents typical values of localised magnetic flux densities produced by some electrical appliances. The fields are highly localised and virtually negligible at other than very short distances from the appliance.

TABLE 3.6 Localised 60 Hz magnetic flux densities produced in the vicinity of some electrical appliances (UNEP/WHO/IRPA, 1987)

Appliances	Magnetic flux density (µT) at a distance of:		
	3 cm	30 cm	100 cm
Refrigerator	0.5 – 1.7	0.01 – 0.25	< 0.01
Dishwasher	3.5 – 20	0.6 – 3	0.07 – 0.3
Laundry washer	8.0 – 50	0.15 – 3	0.01 – 0.15
Laundry dryer	0.3 – 8	0.08 – 0.3	0.02 – 0.06
Electric iron	8 – 30	0.12 – 0.3	0.01 – 0.03
Television set	2.5 – 50	0.04 – 2	0.01 – 0.15
Computer (PC)	0.5 – 3	1	< 0.01
Video display terminal	5.6 – 10	0.45 – 1	0.01 – 0.03
Video recorder	1.5	< 0.01	< 0.01
Slide projector	240	45	< 0.15
Heating pad	10 – 180	0.15 – 0.5	0.01 – 0.25
Cooking stove	1 – 50	0.15 – 0.5	0.01 – 0.04
Microwave oven	73 – 200	4 – 8	0.25 – 0.6
Electric toaster	7 – 18	0.06 – 0.7	< 0.01
Immersion heater 1 kW	12	0.1	< 0.01
Bell transformer	135 – 150	0.06 – 1.1	0.01 – 0.05
Vacuum cleaner	200 – 800	2 – 20	0.13 – 2
Hair dryer	6 – 2000	0.01 – 7	0.01 – 0.3
Food mixer	60 – 700	0.06 – 10	0.02 – 0.25
Electric drill	400 – 800	2 – 3.5	0.08 – 0.2
Can opener	1000 – 2000	3.5 – 30	0.07 – 1
Soldering gun	105 – 200	0.3 – 0.6	< 0.01
Fluorescent desk lamp	40 – 400	0.5 – 2	0.02 – 0.25
Halogen lamp	25 – 80	0.6 – 1.7	0.01 – 0.3
Incandescent desk lamp 60 W	0.1 – 0.2	< 0.01	< 0.01
Electric shaver	15 – 1500	0.08 – 9	0.01 – 0.3
Coffee machine	1 – 2	0.01 – 0.2	< 0.01
Electric clock	300	2.25	< 0.01

ELF magnetic fields are also generated by magnetos associated with petrol engine powered devices such as lawnmowers, strimmers and chainsaws. Few measurement data are available but preliminary data indicate personal exposures up to a few hundred µT are possible when using such equipment or when in close proximity to it.

ELF magnetic fields in homes range from about 10 to a few hundred nT. The long-term time-weighted average field strength measured in 208 homes in the UK (Merchant *et al* 1994) is shown in table 3.7. Similarly the long-term average magnetic flux density exposures for most of the population is in the range 10–100 nT. Only people living very close to or underneath high voltage transmission lines may be exposed to higher values. Measurements inside 43 houses in a city in Germany (Stamm, 1993) showed 24 h average magnetic field strengths between 15 nT and 326 nT with a mean of approximately 60 nT. None of the measurements was influenced by a nearby high voltage powerline.

TABLE 3.7 Magnetic fields recorded in the bedroom of 208 homes in the UK (Merchant *et al* 1994)

Sample	Number	Geometric (arithmetic) mean time-weighted average field strength (nT)
All	208	39 (86)
No high voltage line (≥ = 132 kV) within 100 m	200	36 (51)
High voltage line (≥ = 132 kV) within 100 m	8	153 (973)
No medium voltage line (< 132 kV) within 100 m	177	37 (51)
Medium voltage line (< 132 kV) within 100 m	23	33 (44)
Final distribution main (< 415 V) underground	168	36 (49)
Final distribution main (< 415 V) overhead	32	40 (58)
Detached (no HV line)	67	30 (40)
Semi-detached	79	36 (51)
Terraced	42	41 (57)
Flat	12	63 (74)

In recent years the development of personal magnetic field monitors has improved, figures 3.1 and 3.2. In different European countries there are investigations underway to determine the long-term individual exposure of different groups of the population to magnetic fields. Table 3.8 shows the results from personal monitoring of magnetic field strength during approximately one week.

FIGURE 3.1 Personal magnetic flux density exposure meter. (courtesy of NRPB)

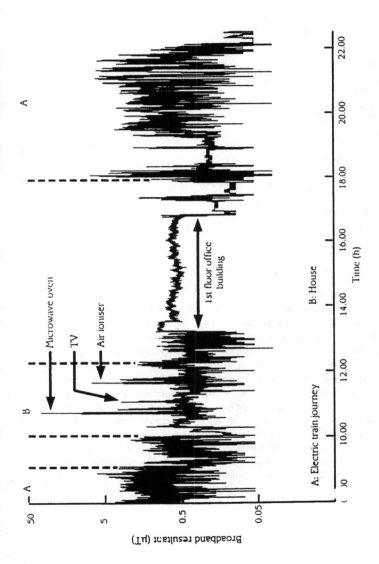

FIGURE 3.2 50 Hz magnetic flux density measurements recorded with an EMDEX personal exposure meter. (courtesy of NRPB)

41

TABLE 3.8 Magnetic field exposure recorded with 214 individuals wearing monitors during one week in the UK (Merchant *et al* 1994)

Sample	Number	Geometric (arithmetic) mean time-weighted average magnetic flux density (nT)
All	214	57 (99)
No high voltage line ($\geq$ = 132 kV) within 100 m	204	54 (70)
High voltage line ($\geq$ = 132 kV) within 100 m	10	208 (686)
No medium voltage line (< 132 kV) within 100 m	183	54 (71)
Medium voltage line (< 132 kV) within 100 m	21	50 (63)
Final distribution main (< 415 V) underground	170	54 (70)
Final distribution main (< 415 V) overhead	34	52 (67)
Detached (no HV line)	66	43 (54)
Semi-detached	85	56 (71)
Terraced	43	60 (76)
Flat	9	109 (128)

Distribution of electric power

Magnetic fields near transmission lines are always linked with electric current flow. The magnetic field beneath high voltage overhead transmission lines is directed mainly transversely to the line axis and depends on the phase relationship between the conductors. Apart from the geometry of the conductor, the maximum magnetic flux density is determined only by the magnitude of the current. The maximum magnetic flux density per unit current at ground level for the most common overhead transmission line systems is approximately 10 to 100 nT A^{-1}. The maximum magnetic flux density at ground level for a double circuit 500 kV overhead transmission lines system is approximately 35 μT kA^{-1}. The maximum ground level magnetic flux densities associated with overhead transmission lines are about 0.01 to 0.05 mT and are also related to line height. High voltage overhead transmission lines represent an extremely extended source where the decrease of field strength down to 10% of the peak value may need distances of more than 50 m depending on the technical design. Typical exposure levels are shown in table 3.9. Data are based on worst case conditions which are not reached during normal operation.

TABLE 3.9 Magnetic fields directly above or under different three-phase power distribution lines

Type of line	Vertical distance (m)	Current (A)	Magnetic flux density (µT)
2 x 123 kV overhead	6	650	20
2 x 245 kV overhead	6.75	1300	30
2 x 420 kV overhead	7.8	2600	55
2 x 420 kV underground	3	1000	30
Medium voltage underground single conductor bundle	1.3	100	0.5
Medium voltage underground single conductor in line	1.3	100	5
Final distribution	1.3	50	0.1
Final distribution; two conductors and no current	1.3	5	0.8

Transport systems

In common railway systems traction currents of several hundred amperes are used. The exact amount depends on the power consumption of the engine needed to accelerate the mass of the train and to overcome all mechanical and dynamic losses. The resulting magnetic fields are therefore highly variable with time. Measurements on the platform of a local city railway showed peak magnetic flux densities up to 30 µT. In general, the magnetic flux density 5 m from the line is approximately 10 µT decreasing to 1 µT at 10 m. Measurements inside a high-speed train in France showed peak values around 6 to 7 µT during high-speed drive (Gourdon 1993). The same field strength was found outside the train at a distance of 10 m.

3.3 Electromagnetic radiation of frequencies between 100 kHz and 300 GHz

3.3.1 Background and terminology

The data presented in this section are restricted to public exposure, therefore sources which give rise to occupational exposure are not considered unless they add appreciably to the electromagnetic environment where the public has access.

Exposure quantities in this section are expressed in one of two different ways depending upon the type of source under investigation. With sources formed from single or multiple monopoles or dipoles, field strengths are quoted, whereas with aperture sources such as dish antennas, power densities are quoted. Field strengths are reported as RMS quantities.

The distance from a source at which the far-field may be regarded to commence is somewhat arbitrary and will depend to a certain extent on the precise electrical structure of the source. In this section the Rayleigh criterion is used for the far-field distance:

$$R_{far} > \frac{2D_{max}^2}{\lambda_{min}}$$

3.1

43

where λ_{min} is minimum wavelength of the radiation from the source and D_{max} is the maximum physical dimension of the source antenna.

Under far-field conditions, the radiated fields from an antenna can be calculated from an expression involving the antenna gain G and the total radiated power P (W). For example, the electric field strength E (V m^{-1}) at a distance r (m) may be obtained from:

$$E \approx \frac{\sqrt{30PG}}{r}$$ 3.2

The power from a point source would be radiated equally in all directions (isotropically) whereas an antenna concentrates the power in particular directions. The degree to which the concentration occurs is represented by the gain of the antenna, G.

The product of the radiated power and the gain is often known as the Equivalent Isotropically Radiated Power (EIRP) because it describes what the total radiated power of the antenna would be if it radiated the same power density in all directions as in its main beam. Where linear antenna systems are used such as in VHF and UHF broadcasting, the gain G is often referred to a simple linear antenna, the half-wave dipole. The product PG is then known as the effective radiated power (ERP). As the gain of a half-wave dipole over an isotropic source is 1.64, the product of PG must be multiplied by 1.64 to obtain EIRP.

When calculating field strengths from sources operating at VHF and higher frequencies it is usual to include the effect of a contribution from a ground reflected wave. Pessimistically this will double the field strength or increase the power density by a factor of four.

The region of space between a source and the far-field is known as the near-field, although it may be considered as consisting of two further regions. At distances less than $\lambda/2\pi$ from a source, reactive field components rapidly predominate over radiated fields causing the wave impedance to become complex and not equal to 377 Ω. This implies a region of stored energy where fields cannot easily be calculated, nor can they easily be transformed to power densities. Field strengths in the reactive near-field of sources are calculated in this section using an antenna analysis program known as Numerical Electromagnetics Code (NEC). This code is well validated and has been used successfully for around ten years by many authors.

The Fresnel near-field region is most relevant for reflector antennas such as dishes used for microwave communications systems or radar where the aperture dimensions are equivalent to many wavelengths. This region exists between the reactive near-field and the far-field and in it the wave impedance is equal to 377 Ω, but power density varies and has an oscillatory dependence upon distance. This is because the distances to the point of exposure from different positions in the radiating aperture are such that they vary by greater than half a wavelength, that is the aperture appears to consist of many Fresnel zones. The point at which a dish antenna appears as a single Fresnel zone is when a separation distance of $D^2/4\lambda$ is reached. If the precise dimensions and excitation functions for a dish are known it is possible to calculate where the maximum power density occurs for a given dish antenna and this is usually inside the Fresnel near-field but close to the far-field boundary.

A conservative estimate of the maximum power density P_{max} (W m^{-2}) in the near-field of a source may be obtained using

$$P_{max} = \frac{4P}{A_e} \qquad\qquad 3.3$$

where A_e (m^2) is the effective aperture (area) of the source and may be calculated from $A_e = G\lambda^2/4\pi$, (λ in m).

3.3.2 Broadcast transmitters

The frequency bands used for broadcasting in the UK by the BBC and independent broadcasters are shown in table 3.10. The approximate number of transmitters, grouped by band and power, is shown in table 3.11 (Allen *et al* 1994).

TABLE 3.10 Broadcasting bands in the UK (Allen *et al* 1994)

Designation	Frequency range	Usage
LF (long wave)	145.5 – 283.5 kHz	Radio
MF (medium wave)	526.5 – 1606.5 kHz	Radio
HF (short wave)	3.9 – 26.1 MHz	International radio
VHF (band II)	87.5 – 108 MHz	FM radio
UHF (band IV–V)	470 – 854 MHz	Television

TABLE 3.11 Broadcast transmitters in the UK (Allen *et al* 1994)

Service	Effective radiated power (ERP for VHF, UHF) or power (kW)					
	0–0.1	0.1–1	1–10	10–100	100–500	>500
MF	5	76	99	21	12	3
HF	0	0	0	0	25	10
VHF FM	100	100	139	2460	25	0
UHF TV	3192	548	228	120	76	16

LF, MF and HF radio

Antennas used for long, medium and short wave radio tend to be vertically polarised monopoles fed at ground level via their bases and vary between 0.1 and 1 wavelength long although most electrical lengths are usually close to a quarter of a wavelength. Antennas as short as a tenth of a wavelength are used at the lowest frequencies because of practical considerations, for example at 150 kHz, the wavelength is 200 m.

At distances greater than a wavelength from these antennas, field strengths become inversely proportional to distance, while at lesser distances, the field strength has a complicated dependence. In this region simple calculations can be unreliable and it is best to measure fields.

Public access to the base of broadcast antennas is restricted but if a person was able to approach to within 30 m of a 0.1 wavelength antenna transmitting at 145 kHz, numerical predictions indicate that exposure to electric fields up to 630 V m^{-1} and magnetic fields up to 1.2 A m^{-1} could occur for a 500 kW ERP transmission. Calculations suggest that for a 50 kW AM (medium wave) radio station fields would be below 10 V m^{-1} at distances in excess of about 200 m, less than 25 V m^{-1} at distances greater than 100 m and less than 275 V m^{-1} at distances greater than 21 m. Measurements at an MF station with two 50 kW and two 75 kW transmitters gave rise to fields of 275 V m^{-1} at 30 m from a 75 kW mast radiator (Allen *et al* 1994).

VHF radio

This frequency band is used for national and local radio; the powers used are rather less than at lower frequencies because each individual transmitter has a smaller coverage area. The antennas are formed from dipole arrays mounted on towers at heights of 10–100 m and their main beams are directed horizontally with a slight downward beam tilt.

Exposure can occur in the main beam of the antennas at large distances or at closer distances from a secondary beam associated with certain types of antenna. This secondary beam or grating lobe is directed downwards to the ground beneath the antenna.

The forward gains of these antennas are up to 10 dB in the main beam and, because this beam is directed horizontally, maximum exposures will occur around head heights or on the upper floors of buildings close to the transmitter. In the main beam of a 100 kW ERP transmitter at a distance of 100 m, the electric and magnetic field strengths can be calculated as 44 V m^{-1} and 0.12 A m^{-1} using the conservatively safe assumption of reinforcement from a ground reflected wave.

UHF television

At UHF frequencies used for TV transmission, wavelengths are in the range from about 0.35 to 0.65 m and propagation is more line of sight than at the broadcast frequencies used for radio. Coverage is therefore achieved by using a small number of high power transmitters mounted on very high towers (300 to 400 m), together with lower power transmitters which give local coverage in some areas.

The high power antennas are formed from dipole arrays and have similar radiation patterns to VHF antennas. They have a main beam which is horizontally directed with a slight downward tilt and a grating lobe which is directed to the foot of the tower. The main beam has a width of 10° to 20° and therefore exposure to it can occur only at distances greater than a kilometre or so from the tower. Calculations give the electric field strength at 1 km from a 1 MW ERP transmitter as 14 V m^{-1} assuming that a wave reflected from the ground arrives in phase with the direct wave.

The grating lobe, which is directed downwards can give rise to a similar field exposure within a few hundred metres of the base of a UHF transmitting tower.

Measurements of the fields from a 1 MW ERP transmitter with antenna mounted at a height of 400 m gave a maximum measured field strength at a distance of 80 m from the tower base of 3 V m^{-1}. Similar measurements on a 100 kW transmitter mounted at a height of 370 m gave a field strength of 0.4 V m^{-1} at a distance of 500 m (Allen and Harlen 1983).

3.3.3 Cellular radio

Cellular radio systems involve communication from hand-held radiotelephones or vehicle mounted transceivers to fixed base stations that each provide coverage of a given area. The communications are full duplex (transmit/receive capability) with a separate RF channel provided for the signal travelling via the uplink to the base station and the downlink back to the mobile. The coverage area of a base station is known as a cell and is ideally hexagonal in shape so a honeycomb mesh of cells can give total coverage. The base station may be at the centre of a cell or at the junction of three cells dependent on the volume of call traffic within the cells. Up to six antennas may be mounted on a given base station to cover different azimuthal sectors. Typical cells range from 1 to 15 km with a limit of about 35 km for the digital communication systems.

From the early 1980s various analogue cellular radio systems have been introduced in Europe with frequency bands around 150, 200, 450 and 900 MHz using channel spacing ranging from 12.5 to 25 kHz. In the absence of a global standard, a variety of systems have appeared, the later being similar to the Total Access Communications System (TACS) which is used in Austria, Ireland, Italy, Spain and the UK. An extension to the normal TACS band is known as ETACS. Analogue systems are widespread throughout Europe and they are expected to remain in existence until early next century when it is envisaged that digital communications will supplant them. Table 3.12 gives frequency bands and channel separations for representative analogue and digital systems.

Digital systems are based upon the harmonised European standard known as GSM, named after the Groupe Spécial Mobile which originally drafted its specification. It is also known as Global System for Mobile communication. The initial frequency allocation for GSM is adjacent to that of the analogue TACS system which will allow the spectrum to be gradually transferred as demand shifts from analogue. A further set of digital communications systems, known as Personal Communication Networks (PCN), is based upon the GSM standard. One such system is known as DCS1800 and operates within a band of frequencies spread around 1.8 GHz as shown in table 3.12.

TABLE 3.12 Frequency bands and channel separations for different cellular radio systems (MUH 1993)

System	Frequency range (MHz)		Channel separation (kHz)	Number of channels
	Uplink	Downlink		
TACS	890–905	935–950	25	600
ETACS	872–888	917–933	25	640
GSM	905–915	950–960	200	50
DCS1800	1710–1785	1805–1880	200	375

An important feature of cellular radio systems is adaptive power control. This is used to ensure that communications are carried out with an adequate signal to noise ratio, but not with unnecessarily high power which could interfere with calls in neighbouring cells and thus reduce the capacity of the network. For the purposes of exposure hazard calculations, it is assumed that the radiated power is equal to the maximum possible, although this is unlikely to occur in practice.

Base stations

The power classes of the various digital base stations are defined in table 3.13. These values refer to powers measured at the input to the base station transmitter combiner and are often referred to as peak powers. The term peak power actually refers to the average power over the burst associated with a given call and the values given in the table are maximum powers with no power derating. The highest permitted analogue base station power for TACS is 100 W (50 dBm).

Typical powers used in practice are not more than 40 W for GSM and 20 W for TACS.

47

TABLE 3.13 Power classes of various digital base stations (ETSI 1992, 1993)

Power class	GSM		DCS1800	
	(W)	(dBm)	(W)	(dBm)
1	320	55	20	43
2	160	52	10	40
3	80	49	5	37
4	40	46	2.5	34
5	20	43		
6	10	40		
7	5	37		
8	2.5	34		

The transmitting antennas of base stations are formed from vertical arrays of colinear dipoles which are phased to give a very narrow vertical beamwidth of around 7° with up to 10° of downward beam tilt so that the main beam is incident on the ground between around 100 m and the edge of the cell. The arrays are often mounted in corner reflectors to give sector antennas with beamwidths of either 60° or 120° in the horizontal plane. Either three or six antennas are then used to provide coverage of a cell in areas of high call traffic, figure 3.3.

For the 900 MHz and 1800 MHz systems, typical wavelengths are around 33 and 16 cm and the maximum antenna dimensions are around 3 and 1.5 m respectively. This gives the far-field distances as 54 m at 900 MHz and 27 m at 1800 MHz.

Base station antennas are either mounted on towers with typical heights in the range 15-50 m or on the roofs or sides of tall buildings. The antenna beams have a downward tilt of less than 10°, therefore public exposure to their main beams should not be possible at radial distances of less than 58 m. Sidelobes have power levels that are at least 20 dB below that of the main beam and therefore need not be considered.

The gain of an omnidirectional antenna is 12 to 14 dB, whereas that of a sector antenna is 16 to 20 dB. Each base station does not transmit on all carriers, but usually has a maximum of less than 10 for the digital systems and less than 40 for TACS. On the basis of an exposure distance of 58 m, a gain of 20 dB and that a reflected wave from the ground adds in phase with the direct wave, it is possible to calculate the fields to which various systems can expose the public, table 3.14.

FIGURE 3.3 Mobile telephone base station. (courtesy of NRPB)

TABLE 3.14 Calculated maximum field strengths from base
stations

System type	Power per carrier (W)	Number of carriers	Field strengths	
			E (V m⁻¹)	H (A m⁻¹)
TACS	20	40	53	0.14
GSM	40	10	38	0.10
DCS1800	20	10	27	0.07

It is emphasised that the calculated values in table 3.14 are worst case theoretical values.
Measurements made upon a system similar to TACS, but in the USA, have found maximum public
exposure levels to be less than 0.2 V m^{-1} per carrier from a system using approximately 12.6 W
radiated power per carrier and an antenna with a gain of 11.15 dB (Peterson and Testagrossa 1992).
Scaling this value to account for a system with 40 carriers each having a radiated power of 20 W
and an antenna gain of 20 dB yields a predicted total electric field strength of 4.4 V m^{-1} for a worst
case practical installation of UK TACS, table 3.14. A similar scaling for GSM using the parameters
shown in table 3.14 gives an electric field strength of 3.1 V m^{-1}.

Where a base station antenna is mounted upon a building or rooftop, it may be possible
to encounter the main beam at distances of only a few metres. In such cases it may be necessary
to control access to the rooftop around the antennas and to impose distances within which persons
should not approach in order to ensure compliance with recommended exposure guidelines.

Mobile transmitters

Mobile transmitters are usually vehicle mounted and there are no physical restrictions to
prevent the public approaching even to within touching distance of them. Persons walking past the
antennas, if exposed, will be so for only a few seconds and, as guidelines allow for averaging over
six minutes, their exposure will be small. Passengers inside vehicles with roof mounted antennas
will be partially shielded from the fields and in the case of antennas mounted at the rear of a car,
separations from rear passengers are likely to exceed 60 cm.

Mobile antennas are not highly directive because their orientation with respect to a base
station is variable. Accordingly, they are usually in the form of simple monopoles mounted above
metal structures such as the body of a car. Such structures have similar gains to half-wave dipoles,
around 2 dB.

Each mobile communication system has a different power class which, due to adaptive
power control, represent maximum transmit powers rather greater than typical levels. These levels
are summarised in table 3.15; however, it must be noted that the digital systems have a duty cycle
of 1/8 because of their Time Division Multiple Access (TDMA) schemes and thus their peak powers
may be proportionally reduced for exposure assessments.

The far-field distances are only between about 2 and 4.3 cm, allowing field strengths for
exposure assessments to be calculated at all but the closest distances. Assuming the maximum
powers listed in table 3.15, compensated for duty cycle where appropriate, antenna gains of 2 dB
and a tolerance of up to 2.5 dB on transmit powers, the maximum field strengths at 10 and 60 cm
are as summarised in table 3.16.

TABLE 3.15 Power classes for mobile transmitters

Power class	TACS (W)	TACS (dBm)	GSM (W)	GSM (dBm)	DCS1800 (W)	DCS1800 (dBm)
1	10	40	20	43	1	30
2	4	36	8	39	0.25	24
3	1.6	32	5	37		
4	0.6	28	2	33		
5			0.8	29		

TABLE 3.16 Maximum field strengths from mobile transmitters

System type	Carrier power (W)	Field strengths and distances E (V m⁻¹) 10 cm	E (V m⁻¹) 60 cm	H (A m⁻¹) 10 cm	H (A m⁻¹) 60 cm
TACS	10	291	48.5	0.770	0.129
GSM	2.5	145	24.2	0.386	0.064
DCS1800	0.125	32.5	5.42	0.086	0.014

Handsets

Handsets are small compact transceivers which are held against the head whilst a call is made. Their electrical structure is normally that of a monopole antenna, or occasionally a sleeve dipole antenna, mounted on a metal box. The user is in the near-field of the source because the distance from the antenna to the head is only about 2 cm. Simple field calculations are not appropriate to assess exposure.

Numerical calculations based upon coupling from handsets to an anatomically realistic numerical phantom of the head have shown that, during normal operation, a radiated power of 1 W gives rise to a maximum Specific Absorption Rate (SAR) of 2.1 W kg⁻¹ at 900 MHz and 3.0 W kg⁻¹ at 1800 MHz averaged over any 10 g of tissue (Dimbylow and Mann 1994).

Typical handset powers are 0.6 W for TACS, 0.25 W for GSM and 0.125 W for DCS 1800 allowing for the duty cycle of GSM and DCS 1800 systems. Tolerances on transmitter power are permitted which for GSM and DCS 1800 are ± 2.5 dB and would result in maximum powers of 0.44 W and 0.22 W respectively. Higher power classes are unlikely to be used for handsets due to the restrictions imposed by the battery power supplies.

3.3.4 Citizens band radio

Citizens band (CB) radio is used in some countries and typical fields produced are as detailed in the following sections. It is important to note that although the field strengths very close to the antennas are likely to exceed field guidelines and limits, they are highly non-uniform reactive fields which do not give rise to the same level of induced currents and heating effects as equivalent plane waves. They also only give rise to exposure over very small regions of the body, usually the extremities, and average whole-body exposure fields will be at least an order of magnitude less.

27 MHz band

The majority of CB radio usage is on the 40 channels spread from 27.60125 to 27.99125 MHz at 10 kHz intervals (Home Office Radio Regulatory Department 1981a). Transmitters are permitted a maximum power of 4 W into a 50 Ω load and they can only be connected to antennas of a single element rod type with a maximum length of 1.5 m. Antennas of this type cannot have gain appreciably greater than a half-wave dipole, 2.15 dB.

The mean wavelength in the 27 MHz band is around 10.8 m and therefore a 1.5 m rod antenna is less than a quarter of a wavelength long. The consequence of this is that 27 MHz antennas are not naturally resonant and loading coils have to be applied to them to force resonance. The most popular position for these coils is at the base of antennas, although certain designs feature coils at their centre or even at their tips.

The near-field of a 1.5 m rod antenna extends to a distance of 42 cm. At distances greater than this from the antenna, its radiated fields may be calculated from simple formulae, but at closer distances, the fields depend upon the precise length and structure of the antenna. Loading coils have a very great effect upon the near-fields of CB antennas with much stronger electric fields existing close to the shorter antennas; however, all lengths of antenna have similar electric fields at greater distances which are in the far-field. Magnetic fields appear to be largely unaffected by the loading coils and are of a similar level for each length of antenna at any distance.

The measured electric field strength at 5 cm from a 112 cm base loaded CB antenna was 990 V m^{-1} (Ruggera 1979), while NEC modelling gave a predicted field of 1139 V m^{-1}. Thus measurement and theory are in reasonable agreement.

CB antennas are often mounted upon the bumpers of cars, on poles outside houses or on mobile handsets which are held close to the heads of users. Fields above guideline levels can exist close to 27 MHz CB antennas at distances less than 50 cm.

934 MHz band

A further permitted band of 20 channels exists from 934.025 to 934.975 MHz with 50 kHz channel separation (Home Office Radio Regulatory Department 1981b). In this band the maximum permitted power from any transmitter with a separate antenna is 8 W into a 50 Ω load. Approved antennas may not have more than four dipole elements, each of which must have a length of less than 17 cm so that the array antenna gain is not greater than 5 dB. The fields from these antennas may be calculated at all but the closest distances by using simple formulae.

Four element dipole arrays are generally mounted several metres above ground with their main beam directed horizontally. Under these conditions, public exposure will not usually be possible at distances of less than 3 m, where the electric and magnetic field strengths will have fallen to 9.1 V m^{-1} and 0.024 A m^{-1} respectively.

Public exposure to vehicle mounted transmitters may occur at much shorter distances of only a few centimetres, although this is only likely to occur for very short periods of time. Vehicle mounted antennas are usually quarter-wave rod antennas, with lengths of around 8 cm.

The field calculations and power constraints thus far mentioned only apply to equipment with a separate antenna; equipment with an integral antenna, such as a CB handset, is limited to an effective radiated power of 3 W, which corresponds to an actual radiated power of 1.8 W. The exposure situation with a device such as this is similar to that described for a GSM handset.

3.3.5   Communications links

Microwave links

Pairs of microwave dish antennas are used to provide line of sight communications links in a variety of applications ranging from public telecommunications and private business communications to digital data links. This is because channel bandwidths are much wider than those used at lower transmission frequencies. It is also possible to produce highly directive dish antennas which can transmit over large distances using low power levels.

The frequencies used for microwave links are usually in the range 5 to 40 GHz and power levels range from less than 1 to a few W but are generally not more than 8 W. Dish antennas are used with diameters ranging from 30 cm to 1 or 2 m, and these achieve gains of 30 to 50 dB in the main beam; however, they also have many sidelobes which may be the more significant in relation to public exposure but the power is usually at least 20 dB below that in the main beam.

The antennas are mounted upon towers, figure 3.4, or the tops of buildings with heights of at least 20 m, thus a typical main beam with a width of 10° cannot intercept the ground at distances of less than 230 m. With a radiated power of 8 W and a gain of 50 dB, the power density would be 2.4 W m^{-2} assuming a ground-reflected component adds in phase. Exposure of the public is also possible from sidelobes which travel more directly to the ground beneath the antenna. Assuming a gain of 10 dB for a sidelobe travelling directly downwards, the power density at 20 m from an 8 W antenna will be 64 mW m^{-2}, under far-field conditions.

Satellite uplinks

Powerful and highly directive transmission systems are used to communicate between Earth stations and satellites which are usually in geostationary orbits. The dish sizes, frequencies, powers and gains of several such systems are shown in table 3.17.

TABLE 3.17 Physical characteristics of some existing satellite uplink stations (Hankin 1986)

Dish diameter (m)	Frequency (GHz)	Power (kW)	Gain (dB)	Far-field distance (km)
64.0	2.38	225	61.9	65.0
32.0	14.25	5	69.0	97.3
25.9	2.38	225	53.8	10.6
18.3	8.15	4	60.8	18.2
13.0	6.00	0.26	56.4	6.8
12.0	6.42	5	55.4	6.2
10.0	5.96	0.2	53.6	4.0
5.45	8.15	4	52.1	1.6
3.05	14.0	1.4	50.0	0.8

Typical EIRPs for the antennas in table 3.17 are from 50 MW to 350 GW, and these result in power densities of significance out to considerable distances, for example the 64 m dish antenna in table 3.17 gives a power density of 2.77 W m^{-2} even at 100 km. The antennas have very high gains ranging from 50.0 to 69.0 dB and these correspond to very narrow main beamwidths ranging from about 1.1 to 0.13°.

FIGURE 3.4 Microwave communications tower (courtesy of NRPB)

54

It is possible to be exposed to power densities of a few hundred W m^{-2} in the near-field of high power satellite stations; however, the antennas are directed at satellites and of necessity nearby buildings and features have to be avoided; consequently exposure in the main lobe is most unlikely to arise under normal circumstances.

3.3.6 Radar

Radar systems use microwave frequencies from 500 MHz up to around 15 GHz, although there are some systems operating up to 100 GHz. The signals produced differ from those of the other sources described in this section in that they are pulsed with very short duty cycles that give average powers which are several orders of magnitude less than the peak powers. Exposure guidelines are based upon thermal effects and therefore it is the mean powers, and thus RMS power densities, that are the relevant parameters. Care has to be taken where measurements are quoted to ensure that these are the values given.

The antennas used for radars are moderately directive with gains ranging from 40 dB to 55 dB and thus their main beams are only a few degrees wide. Many of the systems feature antennas whose direction is continuously varied by either rotating them in azimuth or varying their elevation by a nodding motion.

These considerations further reduce the likelihood of excessive exposure because any member of the public in the vicinity of a radar will only be directly exposed for the brief instant of time that the radar is pointing at them. Typically rotation or nodding will reduce mean power by a factor of 100 and thus reduce RMS fields by a factor of 10.

Acquisition and tracking

These antennas can either rotate to perform a scan or, if they lock on to a target, point in a particular direction for an appreciable length of time. Table 3.18 shows is illustrative of many different types of tracking radar with widely varying source parameters, including the peak and mean (duty cycle corrected) powers. Table 3.19 reports the exposure capabilities of the different systems in two different ways: firstly the maximum power density in the near-field and the distance at which this occurs are given, and the distances to the 1, 10 and 100 W m^{-2} power density contours are presented.

TABLE 3.18 Parameters of tracking radar installations (Hankin 1986)

Radar	Dish diameter (m)	Frequency (GHz)	Source power Peak (kW)	Source power Mean (W)	Gain (dB)
1	1.22	9.8		4670	39.0
2	1.52	34.5	120	59.9	51.8
3	8.78	2.90	10000	3280	45.5
4	10.58	5.84	2500	100	53.2
5	11.43	5.40	3000	120	53.2
6	14.4	9.38	1000	640	60.0
7	26.19	1.30	5000	1500	48.0

Certain tracking radar systems can produce mean power densities greater than 100 W m^{-2} at distances in excess of a kilometre, even after duty cycle correction. In the case of acquisition radar systems which rotate, the effect of rotation reduces the power density measured under stationary conditions by a factor of around 100.

TABLE 3.19 Power densities due to tracking radars (Hankin 1986)

Radar	Near-field distance (m)	Maximum power density (W m^{-2})	Distance to contour (m)		
			100 W m^{-2}	10 W m^{-2}	1 W m^{-2}
1	8.6	8000	108	343	1080
2	47.2	65.7	-	171.1	541.0
3	131.6	108	142.6	612.8	1940
4	384.7	2.3	-	-	820.9
5	415.5	2.3	-	-	899
6	421.6	55.8	-	1410	4450
7	523.3	557	1750	5520	17500

Air traffic control

Air traffic control (ATC) radars are scanning devices which are used to track aircraft flights and control their landings at airports. They rotate through a full 360° arc and therefore produce relatively low mean power densities in any one direction. Also, the powers used tend to be slightly lower than with tracking radars. A summary of ATC radars used in the UK is given in table 3.20.

TABLE 3.20 Air traffic control radars used in the UK (Allen *et al* 1994)

Operating frequency (GHz)	Radar type	Maximum peak power (kW)	Maximum mean power (W)
0.6	S264	70	150
0.6	S264A	500	1000
1.3	HSA/ARJ	75–2200	120–3300
3	Various	60–650	125–600
10	Various	20–150	10–230
15	ASTRE	20	6.5

Measurements have also been made in the vicinity of an ATC radar operating at 2.8 GHz with a peak output power of 650 kW. Measurements made at a height of 9 m with the antenna stationary gave power densities less than 0.5 W m^{-2} at 60 m and 20 W m^{-2} at 19 m. With a rotating antenna, the mean power densities would be lower.

Marine

Marine radar equipment ranges from large installations of supertankers to the smaller mast mounted equipment used by yachts. Utilisation of the systems is also variable with the larger installations of cross-channel ferries being operated continuously while the battery-powered equipment of small-boat radars is only used intermittently. Generally the powers are rather lower than other radar systems with peak powers of up to 30 kW and mean powers ranging from around 1 to 25 W. Under normal operating conditions with the antenna rotating, the average power density of the higher power systems within a metre of the turning circle of the radar system can be calculated to be less than 10 W m^{-2}.

3.3.7 Microwave ovens

Microwave ovens operate at a frequency of 2.45 GHz with powers of most domestic ovens in the range 600–1000 W. Very high power densities occur within the sealed cavities of ovens but manufacturing standards require that leakage should be kept below emission limits. Standards generally specify that leakage should be less than 50 W m^{-2} at a distance of 5 cm from the external surfaces of the appliance. In practice, modern microwave ovens meet these requirements easily and most ovens would not be expected to leak above 10 W m^{-2}. Ergonometric studies have shown that the average distance of a microwave user is between 0.7 and 2 m from their oven. Assuming that a leaking door behaves as a slot antenna and that its fields decay according to the inverse square of the distance, it may be calculated that the power density at 1 m arising from leakage of 10 W m^{-2} is 0.25 mW m^{-2}.

In a survey of 357 microwave ovens used in the catering industry of which most were of the domestic type, only 6 ovens indicated leakage at 5 cm above 10 W m^{-2} and only 1 oven exceeded 50 W m^{-2} (HELA 1989). The ovens which gave rise to measurable leakage were mostly between 1 and 7 years old and the age of the oven was not shown to be a major factor in the extent of leakage.

A survey of 130 microwave ovens in domestic use (Matthes 1992) showed that all ovens emitted less than 10 W m^{-2} at 5 cm and a statistical analysis indicated that 50% of ovens would emit less than 1 W m^{-2}.

3.4 Visible and infrared radiation

Natural sources of non-coherent optical radiation include the sun (incandescence), lightning (electrical discharge) and luminescence (both chemical and biological). Radiation from the sun is the most important in providing illumination and IRR. The spectral distribution from the sun approximates to that of a black body radiator at a temperature of 5900 K. However, the spectrum at the Earth's surface is modified by many factors such as atmospheric absorption and scattering, atmospheric turbidity and pollutants, cloud cover, altitude and the sun's zenith angle. Under clear sky conditions, the illuminance at the Earth's surface can exceed 100 klux (Cullen and Chou 1992).

Lightning produces ionised plasma at temperatures of about 30,000 K but for only a few milliseconds. Optical radiation, including visible and IRR, represents less than 1% of the emitted electromagnetic radiation. The radiance and luminance of natural luminescent sources are so low as to be considered insignificant (Cullen and Chou 1992).

Artificial sources of non-coherent optical radiation include incandescent filament sources, discharge lamps, welding flames and arcs, and solid state emitters, such as light emitting diodes

(Sliney and Wolbarsht 1980, McKinlay *et al* 1988, Cullen and Chou 1992). Members of the public can obtain consumer products using a wide range of optical radiation sources for lighting, heating, entertainment and display (Pearson *et al* 1991). Products incorporating incandescent optical radiation sources are used for lighting (such as in tungsten and tungsten halogen luminaires), for heating (such as in space heaters and radiant hotplates) and for special purposes (such as in flash photography). Products incorporating discharge lamps are used for general lighting (such as general purpose and compact fluorescent tubes), for cosmetic purposes (such as in sunlamps and sunbeds) and for special purposes (such as horticultural lamps and black lights for entertainment and display).

Over the years incandescent sources have undergone many modifications and improvements in the design and composition of the filaments, the filling medium, the envelope and the holder/reflector unit. Almost all incandescent lamps nowadays use tungsten filaments (which may be alloyed with rhenium or thorium) because of its properties of strength, low cost, relatively high melting point and low vapour pressure. Tungsten halogen lamps, incorporating a halogen (usually iodine) as a filling gas, have become popular because of their improved luminous efficacy and longer life, figure 3.5. A filament source emits a spectrum which approximates to that of a black body at the same temperature. The higher the temperature of operation of the filament, the higher will be the blue-light emission from the source (envelope permitting). Tungsten filaments operate at temperatures between 2700 and 3000 K and the peak emission is at the red end of the visible spectrum. Filaments in tungsten halogen lamps operate at higher temperatures (2900 to 3450 K) with a resulting higher emission at the blue end of the visible spectrum. Infrared heating incandescent lamps operate in the temperature range 2000 to 2500 K and produce little visible radiation (Cullen and Chou 1992).

The electrical discharge in a gas is utilised as a source of optical radiation, found in both occupational and non-occupational environments. The gas is usually a mixture of an inert gas and mercury or sodium vapour. The general lighting fluorescent lamp, using a mercury low pressure discharge to stimulate emissions from a phosphor coating on the inner surface of the glass envelope, is the most commonly encountered discharge device. These lamps emit a number of discrete lines (from the low pressure mercury discharge) on a spectral continuum (produced by the phosphor coating). A range of phosphors is available which allows a large selection of near white and other colours. They do not represent a retinal thermal injury and under normal conditions of operation do not represent a potential blue-light hazard (McKinlay *et al* 1988).

Low pressure mercury lamps are used in a wide range of other applications, primarily in relation to UVR emissions, such as germicidal lamps for sterilisation. The fluorescent black light, used for entertainment, display and material testing, is a low pressure mercury discharge lamp with a Woods' glass envelope, allowing high UVR transmission and low visible transmission. These lamps employ a phosphor which has a peak emission at about 370 nm in the UVA; the UVB emissions from these lamps are low. Low pressure mercury discharge lamps are also used in sunbeds and for clinical purposes using phosphors specifically manufactured to produce primarily UVR. Older tanning systems may use high pressure mercury vapour discharge lamps which do not have a phosphor, depending solely on the mercury discharge to produce UVR with a greater component at shorter wavelengths. Medium pressure mercury lamps are used, for example, in photocopiers and sunlamps (McKinlay *et al* 1988, Cullen and Chou 1992).

Low and high pressure sodium discharge lamps are frequently used for street and area lighting because of their high luminous efficacy and long service life. Although the peak spectral emission of high pressure sodium lamps is in the yellow-green region of the visible spectrum, the luminance and blue-light radiance can be comparable with that from high pressure mercury general lighting lamps, due to the non-diffusing outer envelopes used with sodium lamps. Advertising tube (neon) lamps are low pressure discharge lamps usually filled with neon (red), krypton (yellow) or argon (blue), the characteristics of the filling gas determining the colour of the emission (Cullen and Chou 1992).

FIGURE 3.5 Conventional tungsten and tungsten halogen lamps.
(courtesy of NRPB)

Members of the public may be exposed to welding sources, although these are generally associated with occupational exposure. There are many and varied welding processes and the optical radiation emitted by each varies widely both in quantity and spectral composition. Torch brazing and gas welding operations (including oxyacetylene welding) produce flames which have a high infrared component. The visible radiation hazards from gas welding procedures are considered to be minimal. However, the emissions from unshielded arc welding processes can be very high and may represent a corneal as well as a retinal hazard. Carbon arcs have been used extensively in projectors, spotlights and searchlights and may represent a potential blue-light retinal hazard. However, they have been substantially replaced nowadays by compact (mercury and xenon) arc lamps which together with linear arc lamps, constitute a significant blue-light and thermal retinal hazard (Sliney and Wolbarsht 1980, Cullen and Chou 1992).

Solid state lamps include many low luminance devices, such as tritiated phosphors, electro- and chemi-luminescent lamps, which are not considered to represent an optical radiation hazard. However, light emitting diodes (LEDs), which are similar to laser diodes except for lower irradiance levels of optical radiation, may represent a retinal hazard in some situations.

A summary of the approximate characteristics of some typical optical radiation sources, based on measured irradiance values between 400 and 1400 nm (the retinal hazard spectral region) is given in table 3.21.

TABLE 3.21 Range of retinal irradiances (W m^{-2}) and radiances (W m^{-2} sr^{-1}) for a variety of optical sources (after Sliney and Wolbarsht 1980)

Optical source	Radiance (W m^{-2} sr^{-1})	Absorbed retinal irradiance (W m^{-2})
Laser (1 W into eye)	-	10^9–10^{10}
Laser (1 mW into eye)	-	10^6–10^7
Lightning bolt	$8\ 10^8$	-
Xenon short arc searchlight (20 kW)	$3\ 10^7$	10^6–10^7
Sun	$1.3\ 10^7$ (at zenith)	10^4–10^5
Electronic photoflash	$\approx 10^7$	-
Electric welding or carbon arc	$\approx 10^6$	10^4–10^5
Sodium arc lamp	$5\ 10^5$	-
Tungsten iodide lamp (1 kW)	$2.5\ 10^5$	-
Tungsten filament	10^5	10^2–10^3
Flashlight (3 V)	$\approx 10^4$	-
Pyrotechnic flare	-	10^2–10^3
Frosted incandescent lamp	$\approx 5\ 10^3$	1–10
Fluorescent high intensity discharge lamp	$\approx 10^3$	-
Snow field at noon	250	-
Candle flame	100	10^{-1}–1
Oxyacetylene torch	40–100	-
Fluorescent lamp	≈ 10	10^{-1}–1
Television screen	-	10^{-3}–10^{-2}
Electroluminescent display	-	10^{-4}–10^{-3}

3.5 Ultraviolet radiation

3.5.1 Solar radiation

Humans have evolved and have been required to acclimatise to an optical radiation environment dominated by the sun. With respect to the emission of optical radiation the sun approximates to a black-body emitter with a temperature of about 5900 K. The principal source of optical radiation within the sun is that part of the solar atmosphere called the photosphere, although the higher and much hotter layers, the chromosphere and the corona, contribute ultraviolet radiation as well as being the source of the sun's x-rays. The mean irradiance just outside the Earth's atmosphere is approximately 1370 W m^{-2} (the so-called ` solar constant') with an approximately $\pm 3\%$ variation depending on the distance of the Earth from the sun; the spectral distribution is shown in table 3.22. Values at the Earth's surface are lower because of attenuation by the atmosphere whose effective thickness (with respect to the path travelled by solar radiation to an observer on the ground) varies with the angle of elevation of the sun. The air attenuation is lowest, therefore, when the sun is high in the sky and at a maximum for the rising or setting sun. Solar irradiance and particularly the short wavelength components, ie UVR and blue light, depend on solar elevation.

This in turn depends not only on latitude, time of day and time of year but on altitude, cloud cover and the degree of air pollution. Attenuation is most marked due to the absorption by ozone (particularly at wavelengths shorter than 300 nm) and by water vapour (in the infrared). As a consequence of the former, solar radiation of wavelengths shorter than about 290 nm does not reach the surface of the Earth. The presence of clouds plays a significant role in attenuating UVR. UVB and UVA irradiances are reduced due to scattering by water droplets and/or ice crystals in the clouds; the magnitude of such scattering processes is essentially independent of wavelength over the UVR range. Clouds provide their largest attenuation in winter when the fraction of sky likely to be covered by them is highest and when the paths travelled by UVR through them are greatest. In summer the values of UVR irradiances are likely to be much closer to those calculated for clear sky conditions.

TABLE 3.22 Spectral distribution of solar UVR prior to attenuation by the Earth's atmosphere (Frederick et al 1989)

Wavelength range	Irradiance* (W m^{-2})	Percentage of total
UVC	6.4	0.5
UVB	21.1	1.5
UVA	85.7	6.3
Total UVR	113.2	8.3

* Visible and infrared radiation together contribute 1254 W m^{-2} (the remaining 91.7%).

3.5.2 Lamps

Lamps can be conveniently grouped under two broad headings: those that produce radiation by incandescence and those that produce it by an electrical (gaseous) discharge. The latter can be sub-divided according to the pressure of the filling gas into those (generally low pressure) lamps that emit primarily within narrow wavebands (so-called line-emissions) and those that emit broad-band (so-called continuum) radiation. The bandwidth of the emission from a gaseous discharge is dependent on the pressure of the gas and, because of this and the possible presence of specific

significantly greater than the average value of ACGIH weighted UVB found in the British study ($7\ 10^{-5}\ W\ m^{-2}_{eff}$). The emissions from some of the so-called super high output (SHO) tubes examined in the American study displayed the presence of 253.7 nm radiation. It has been suggested that this might have been due to a low iron content in the glass envelope of these lamps. The spectral transmission of the glass envelope has been shown to be particularly important in attenuating UVR.

`Special' applications fluorescent lamps

As well as a number of special colour-rendering fluorescent lamps which are essentially variants of general lighting fluorescent lamps, a number of special applications fluorescent lamps have been developed and are commercially available. An example is the so-called blacklight lamp which uses a nickel/cobalt oxide (Woods' glass) envelope. The phosphor chosen emits around 370 nm in the UVA. Woods' glass is almost entirely opaque to light and the lamps are used for a number of commercial, scientific, medical and industrial fluorescence purposes as well as for display and entertainment.

The development of a range of phosphors with enhanced UVA emissions has led to the widespread use of fluorescence lamps for cosmetic tanning. The spectral emissions of two types of lamps commonly used for this purpose are illustrated in figure 3.7. Special types of UVB emitting fluorescence lamps have also been developed, figure 3.8.

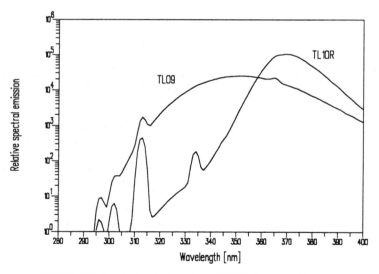

FIGURE 3.7 Spectral emissions from `UVA' fluorescent lamps, Philips types: TL09 and TL10R (McKinlay 1992)

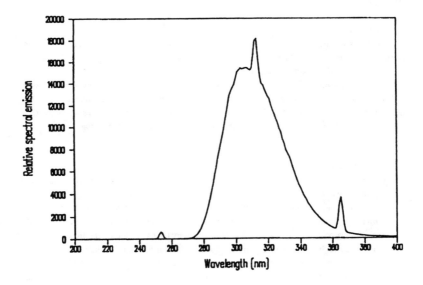

FIGURE 3.8 Spectral emission from a ` UVB' fluorescent lamp

High intensity discharge (HID) lamps

The designation ` high intensity discharge' (HID) lamps includes the families of lamps often called high pressure mercury vapour, metal halide and high pressure sodium vapour lamps. Only mercury vapour and metal halide lamps emit significant amounts of UVR.

High pressure mercury vapour lamps

High pressure mercury vapour lamps are widely used for industrial and commercial lighting, street lighting, display lighting, floodlighting and a large number of printing, curing and other industrial applications. The visible spectral emissions of the discharge are in the blue, green and yellow regions of the spectrum with major emission lines at 436, 546, 577 and 579 nm, and a large amount of UVR is also generated. The general construction of high pressure mercury lamps is a fused silica (quartz) discharge tube containing the mercury/argon vapour discharge mounted inside an outer envelope of soda-lime or borosilicate glass.

The outer glass envelope effectively absorbs most residual UVR; consequently the quantity of potentially harmful UVR emitted by such lamps depends critically on the integrity of this envelope. In the USA, it is a legally enforceable manufacturing requirement that either breakage of the outer envelope must cause the lamp to fail to operate, in which case the lamp is described as self-extinguishing and is marked with the letter "T", or if not self-extinguishing it should be marked with the letter "R". In the latter case a warning notice must be included with the packaging of the lamp (FDA 1988).

Medical lamps

High pressure mercury vapour lamps have also been used for many years for medical treatment purposes, predominantly in the treatment of certain skin diseases, notably psoriasis and acne, and of pressure sores and superficial ulcers.

Another common range of medical applications of high pressure mercury lamps is their use with a Woods' filter for diagnosing such disorders as tinea capitis by UVA-induced fluorescence. The use of high pressure mercury lamps for the UVA-photopolymerising of dental resins was at one time common but has now been replaced by the combined use of tungsten halogen lamps and blue light sensitive resins.

Metal halide lamps

The family of ` metal halide' lamps encompasses a number of different types of high pressure mercury lamps whose discharges all contain additives. The additives are most typically metal halides chosen to produce either a strongly coloured emission (usually a single halide), to produce a more broadly spectrally uniform emission (multi-halide) or to enhance the UVR (most often UVA) emission. Compared with ` ordinary' high pressure mercury lamps the luminous efficacies of metal halide lamps are high. They are used for a range of industrial and commercial applications that include photochemical processing, graphic and photographic illumination, studio lighting, reprography and are also used for UVA cosmetic tanning equipment, for some medical applications and for solar radiation simulation. Figure 3.9 illustrates the effect of protective filters in eliminating hazardous UVR from the emissions of a blue-light phototherapy system incorporating metal halide lamps.

3.5.3   Gas and arc welding

Gas welding

Gas welding, brazing and cutting processes operate at relatively low black body temperatures and their emissions of UVR are low (Moss and Murray 1979).

Arc welding

In comparison with gas welding processes, the emissions of optical radiations from arc welding are very high. Many data on the optical radiation emissions associated with a variety of electric arc welding processes have been published (for example, Lyon et al 1976, Marshall et al 1979, Sliney and Wolbarsht 1980, Mariutti and Matzeu 1988).

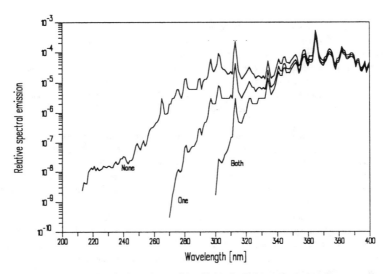

FIGURE 3.9 **Spectral emissions from a blue-light phototherapy system incorporating metal halide lamps. The system is fitted with 2 filters and the measurement data illustrated are for none, one or both filters in place. (McKinlay 1992)**

3.5.4 Lasers

Lasers are used increasingly in areas, such as retail, entertainment and display, where exposure to members of the public is possible. However, in most cases the chance of incurring injury from the laser application is low due to the limited output power from the laser system. The most popular types of lasers include helium-neon and ion lasers and laser diodes, which are used in applications such as entertainment and display and medical areas.

Laser radiation is coherent. The emitted photons are in-phase (temporally coherent) and appear to the eye to have been generated from a point source (spatially coherent) and therefore can be focused by simple lenses, for example the eye, to form a very small spot size. They are also (generally) monochromatic, uni-directional and have the same polarisation and velocity. A laser beam has (generally) a low divergence (ie, it travels in near-parallel lines from its source). These combined properties can result in very high power densities in the beam. Various solids, liquids, gases and diode junctions can act as laser active media, allowing the achievement of stimulated emission at distinct wavelengths throughout the UVR, visible and IRR spectrum. Depending on the active medium and system design, the emission duration can vary from single pulses of duration less than 10^{-13} s to a continuous wave. Commonly used lasers emit power levels that range from a few microwatts to several kilowatts and pulsed radiation can vary greatly in the duration, energy and repetition frequency of the pulses. Particular exceptions to monochromaticity are dye lasers and particular exceptions to highly collimated beams are semiconductor lasers and laser arrays.

3.6 Summary

3.6.1 Static and slowly time varying fields

Static and slowly time varying electric fields in the human environment can reach field strengths of the order of tens of kV m^{-1} from both natural and artificial sources. Static and slowly time varying magnetic fields are also a permanent environmental factor. In general, the Earth's magnetic field is dominant in this frequency range. Natural field strengths are exceeded only in certain situations, for example inside some DC driven public transportation systems. There, magnetic flux densities can reach values of the order of 50 µT to 10 mT.

3.6.2 Time varying electromagnetic fields of frequencies less than 100 kHz

In the frequency range below 100 kHz the dominant exposure of the public results from the use of electric power. The main frequency in Europe for this purpose is 50 Hz.

Relevant exposure to electric fields is only possible in the vicinity of high voltage overhead transmission lines, depending on the distance to the line and the line voltage. Maximum field strengths under transmission lines are 1 to 2 kV m^{-1} for 110 kV lines, 2 to 3 kV m^{-1} for 245 kV lines, 5 to 6 kV m^{-1} for 380 kV lines, and 7 to 8 kV m^{-1} for 400 kV lines.

Magnetic field exposures measured on an individual basis in general are very low for the public ranging between 10 and a few hundred nT. People living within 100 m of high voltage transmission lines may be exposed to fields at the higher end of this range. The maximum magnetic flux density under transmission lines is 10 to 40 µT.

Near electrical appliances, magnetic fields may vary up to 10 µT or more, but local variability of such fields is very high. Thus field strengths reduce quickly with increasing distance to the source.

3.6.3 Electromagnetic fields and radiation of frequencies between 100 kHz and 300 GHz

VLF and MF broadcast antennas can produce the most significant exposure of the public to radiofrequency radiation although access to sites is restricted. Several hundred V m^{-1} at distances up to 30 m is typical. Antennas used for television and radio at VHF and UHF frequencies should not usually give rise to significant public exposure. Maximum field strengths to which the public are exposed are a few V m^{-1}.

Cellular base stations can potentially produce fields of a few tens of V m^{-1} if all of their channels operate simultaneously. However, this is highly unlikely to occur and measurements indicate that maximum exposures in practice would be considerably below 10 V m^{-1}. Mobile transmitters on cars can generate fields of several hundred V m^{-1} at distances less than 10 cm; however, fields inside the vehicles are less than 30 V m^{-1}.

CB antennas can give fields up to 1 kV m^{-1} at distances of a few centimetres, although the fields are highly non-uniform, reactive and exposure is likely to be limited to extremities. Vehicle mounted transmitters should give less than 30 V m^{-1} inside a car.

Radar installations can produce power densities greater than 100 W m^{-2} in their main beams but when radars are rotating, the RMS power density will be reduced by a factor of around 100.

3.6.4 Optical radiation

For most people the major source of UVR exposure is the sun. However, for some individuals, for at least some of the time, UVR from artificial sources may contribute significantly to their total exposure. Such sources include those used for medical therapy, cosmetic tanning and a few industrial sources.

Incandescent sources such as tungsten filament bulbs generally emit levels of UVR insignificant to human health, although some unshielded tungsten halogen lamps can emit amounts of UVR sufficient to cause erythema.

General lighting fluorescent lamps intended for domestic use are specifically designed to emit light and emit very small amounts of UVR. However, special application fluorescent lamps, such as those used for medical and cosmetic tanning, emit levels of UVR sufficient to cause skin and eye injury. The most powerful artificial sources of UVR, and particularly of UVB and UVC, are those characterised as high intensity discharge (HID) lamps. These include high pressure mercury, mercury metal halide and xenon lamps. HID lamps used for lighting purposes are double envelope lamps whose outer envelope attenuates the UVR emitted and, when used within properly designed luminaires, do not present a UVR hazard. Any HID lamps used in an open situation without secondary containment is likely to constitute a UVR hazard.

Gas welding, brazing and cutting processes operate at temperatures insufficiently high to cause the emission of intense UVR, although at close distances and for long exposure times, advised limits for protection may be approached and possibly exceeded. Visible radiation and IRR present a potential hazard to the eyes. Arc welding processes are particularly potent sources of UVR and even exposures of the order of a few seconds may be hazardous to the eyes and to the skin of the operator and of any onlooker. Welding arcs also emit light and infrared radiation hazardous to the retina even when viewed at some distance.

References

ACGIH. 1989. *Threshold limit values for chemical substances and physical agents in the workroom environment.* Cincinnati, American Conference of Governmental Industrial Hygienists.

Allen, S G. 1991. Radiofrequency field measurements and hazard assessment. *J. Radiol. Prot.*, 11, 49–62.

Allen, S G, and Harlen, F. 1983. Sources of exposure to radiofrequency and microwave radiations in the UK. Chilton, NRPB-R144 (London, HMSO).

Allen, S G, Blackwell, R P, Chadwick, P J, Driscoll, C M H, Pearson, A J, Unsworth, C, and Whillock, M J. 1994. Review of occupational exposure to optical radiation and electric and magnetic fields with regard to the proposed CEC Physical Agents Directive. Chilton, NRPB-R265, (London HMSO).

Bernhardt, J H. 1988. Extremely low frequency (ELF) electric fields. IN *Non-ionising Radiation Physical Characteristics, Biological Effects and Health Hazard Assessment.* Proceedings of the International Non-ionising Radiation Workshop, Melbourne, April 1988 (Repacholi, M H, ed). Yallambie, Victoria, Australian Radiation Laboratory, pp 235–253 and 273–289.

Cole, C A, Forbes, P D, Davies, R E, and Urbach, F. 1986. Effects of indoor lighting on normal skin. New York, New York Academy of Sciences Report.

Cullen, A P, and Chou, B R. 1992. Non-coherent optical sources. 1992. IN: *Non-ionising radiation.* Proceedings of the 2nd Non-ionising Radiation Workshop (Wayne-Greene, M, ed). International Radiation Protection Association, pp 307–319.

Dimbylow, P J, and Mann, S M. 1994. SAR calculations in an anatomically realistic model of the head for mobile communication transceivers at 900 MHz and 1.8 GHz. Phys. Med. Biol., 39, 1537-1553.

Dolezalek, H. 1979. Atmospheric electricity. IN *Handbook of Chemistry and Physics*, Cleveland, Chemical Rubber Publishing Co.

ETSI. 1992. ETSI-GSM technical specifications: PHASE 1, Document 0.5.05: Radio transmission and reception. European Telecommunications Standards Institute.

ETSI. 1993. ETSI-GSM technical specifications: PHASE 1, Document 05.05-DCS: Radio transmission and reception. European Telecommunications Standards Institute.

FDA. 1988. Performance standards for light emitting products: paragraph 1040.30. IN *Regulations for the Administration and Enforcement of the Radiation Control for Health and Safety Act of 1968*. Rockville, CDRH, HHS publication FDA 88–8035.

Frederick, J E, Snell, H E, and Haywood, E K. 1989. Solar ultraviolet radiation at the Earth's surface. *Photochem. Photobiol.*, **50**, No. 8, 433–450.

Gourdon, C G. 1993. Efforts of French railroads to reduce traction electromagnetic fields. IN *Electricity and Magnetism in Biology and Medicine*. San Francisco, San Francisco Press, 259–263.

Grandolfo, M, and Vecchia, P. 1985. Natural and man-made environmental exposures to static and ELF electromagnetic fields. IN *Biological Effects and Dosimetry of Static and ELF Electromagnetic Fields* (Grandolfo, M, Michaelson, S M, and Rindi, A, eds). New York and London, Plenum Press.

Grandolfo, M, Michaelson, S M, and Rindi, A (eds). 1985. *Biological Effects and Dosimetry of Static and ELF Electromagnetic Fields*. New York and London, Plenum Press.

Grandolfo, M, Vecchia, P, Angelini, V, Chiotti, E, Ranghiasci, C, Matiussi, R, Battisti, S, and Stoppoloni, P. 1989. Magnetic field strengths in the high speed train ETR450. IN *Proceedings of the 26th National Congress of the Italian Radiation Protection Association*, AIRP (in Italian).

Hankin, N N. 1986. The radiofrequency radiation environment: Environmental exposure levels and RF radiation emitting sources. Washington DC, United States Environmental Protection Agency, EPA 520/1-85-014.

HELA. 1989. Microwave oven leakage – survey. London, Health and Safety Executive, Microwaves/Radiation data sheet HSE 100/11.

Home Office Radio Regulatory Department. 1981a. Performance specification: Angle modulated 27 MHz radio equipment for use in the Citizens Band radio service. London, HMSO, MPT 1320.

Home Office Radio Regulatory Department. 1981b. Performance specification: Angle modulated 934 MHz radio equipment for use in the Citizens Band radio service. London, HMSO, MPT 1321.

Krause, N. 1986. Exposure of people to static and time variable magnetic fields in technology, medicine, research and public life; dosimetric aspects. IN *Biological Effects of Static and ELF-Magnetic Fields*, BGA-Schriftenreihe 3/86. (Bernhardt, J H, ed). Munich, MMV Medizin Verlag, pp 57–71.

Lyon, T L, Sliney, D H, Marshall, W J, Krial, N P, and Deltalle, P H. 1976. Evaluation of the potential hazards from actinic ultraviolet radiation generated by electric welding and cutting arcs. Maryland, US Army Environmental Hygiene Agency Report No. 42-0053-77.

Mariutti, G, Matzeu, M. 1988. Measurement of ultraviolet radiation emitted from welding arcs. *Health Physics*, **54**, No 5, 529–532.

Marshall, W J, Sliney, D H, Hoikkala, M, and Moss, C E. 1979. Optical radiation levels produced by air carbon arc cutting processes. Cincinnati, US Department of Health Education and Welfare Report, National Institute for Occupational Health.

Matthes, R. 1992. Radiation emission from microwave ovens. *J. Radiol. Prot.*, **12**, No. 3, 167–172.

McKinlay, A F. 1992. Artificial sources of UVA radiation: Uses and emission characteristics. IN *Biological Responses to UVA Radiation*, (Urbach, F, ed). Valdenmar Pub. Corp. Kansas.

McKinlay, A F, and Diffey, B L. 1987. A reference action spectrum for ultraviolet induced erythema in human skin. *CIE J.* 6, No 1, 17–22.

McKinlay, A F, Harlen, F, and Whillock, M J. 1988. *Hazards of Optical Radiation - A Guide to Sources, Uses and Safety.* Bristol and Philadelphia, Adam Hilger.

McKinlay, A F, Whillock, M J, and Meulemans, C C E. 1989. Ultraviolet radiation and blue-light emissions from spotlights incorporating tungsten halogen lamps. Chilton, NRPB-R228 (London, HMSO).

Merchant, C J, Renew, D C, and Swanson, J. 1994. Exposure to power-frequency magnetic fields in the home. *J. Radiol. Prot.*, 14, 1, 77–87.

Moss, C E, and Murray, W E. 1979. Optical radiation levels produced by gas welding, torch brazing and oxygen cutting. *Welding J.*, 58, No. 9, 37–46.

MUH. 1993. *Mobile Users Handbook.* (Corby, M E, ed). London, Commercial Ed. Publishing.

Pearson, A J, Grainger, K J L, Whillock, M J, and Driscoll, C M H. 1991. Hazard assessment of optical radiation sources used in some consumer products. *Radiol. Prot. Bull.*, No. 126, 7–14.

Petersen, R C, and Testagrossa, P A. 1992. Radio-frequency electromagnetic fields associated with cellular-radio cell-site antennas. *Bioelectromagnetics*, 13, 527–542.

Polk, C. 1974. Propagation, amplitude and temporal variation of extremely low frequency (0–100 Hz) electromagnetic fields. IN *Biologic and Clinical Effects of Low-frequency Magnetic and Electric Fields.* (Llaurado, J G, Sances, A, Jr, and Battocletti, J H, eds). Springfield, Thomas Publisher.

Ruggera, P S. 1979. Measurements of electromagnetic fields in the close proximity of CB antennas. Washington DC, Bureau of Radiological Health, US Department of Health, Education and Welfare, Food and Drug Administration, HEW Publication (FDA) 79-8080.

Sliney, D H, and Wolbarsht, M L. 1980. *Safety with Lasers and Other Optical Sources.* New York and London, Plenum Press.

Stamm, A. 1993. Untersuchungen zur Magnetfeldexposition der Bevölkerung im Niederfrequenten Bereich. IN *Elektromagnetische Verträglichkeit biologischer Systeme.* (Brinkmann, K and Schaefer, H, eds). Berlin and Offenbach, VDE Verlag. (In German)

Stuchly, M A, 1986. Exposure to static and time-varying magnetic fields in industry, medicine, research and public life; dosimetric aspects. IN *Biological Effects of Static and ELF-magnetic Fields*, BGA-Schriftenreihe 3/86. (Bernhardt, J H, ed). Munich, MMV Medizin Verlag, pp 39–56.

Swanson, J. 1994. Measurements of static magnetic fields in homes in the UK and their implication for epidemiological studies of exposure to alternating magnetic fields. *J. Radiol. Prot.*, 14, No. 1, 67–75.

UNEP/WHO/IRPA. 1984. *Extremely low frequency (ELF) fields. Environmental Health Criteria 35.* Geneva, World Health Organization.

UNEP/WHO/IRPA. 1987. *Magnetic fields. Environmental Health Criteria 69.* Geneva, World Health Organization.

Whillock, M J, Clark, I, McKinlay, A F, Todd, C, and Mandy, S. 1988. Ultraviolet radiation levels associated with the use of fluorescent general lighting, UVA and UVB lamps in the workplace and home. Chilton, NRPB-R221 (London, HMSO).

Zaffanella, L E, and Deno, D W. 1978. Electrostatic and electromagnetic effects of ultra-high-voltage transmission lines. Palo Alto, Electric Power Research Institute Final Report, EPRI EL-802.

4   Biological effects

In this chapter, as the interactions of electromagnetic fields with biological tissues differ in different regions of the spectrum, the biological effects are discussed under four separate sections viz: (a) static and slowly time varying electric and magnetic fields (b) time varying electromagnetic fields of frequencies less than 100 kHz (c) fields and radiation of frequencies between 100 kHz and 300 GHz, and (d) optical radiation.

An extensive and diverse literature has arisen during the last two decades in which a wide variety of biological effects and responses have been attributed to exposure to electromagnetic fields. Many of these effects are known to result from the induction of surface electric charge, induced electric fields and currents within the body, or from increases in thermal loading and elevated body and tissue temperature. These particular effects and responses are well-understood and have been used by various national and international organisations as scientific bases in recommending restrictions on exposure to electromagnetic fields for human populations (IRPA/INIRC 1988 and 1990, Allen *et al* 1991, NRPB 1993). Other biological effects, such as possible adverse effects on pregnancy outcome or an increased risk of certain types of cancer, have been reported following exposure to very low levels of electromagnetic fields. However, these effects are not well established and have not served as a basis for guidance on exposure. There is a greater consensus about the biological effects of optical radiation.

4.1   Static and slowly time varying fields

The biological effects of exposure to static electric and magnetic fields have been extensively reviewed (UNEP/WHO/IRPA 1984 and 1987, Kowalczuk *et al* 1991, and NRPB 1992).

4.1.1   Electric fields

Static and slowly time varying electric fields interact with people in two important ways:

- they act on the outer surface of the body. This may be accompanied by hair movement and other sensory stimulation. It was reported in a study of volunteers exposed to static electric fields of up to 40 kV m^{-1} that there was a threshold of perception around 20 kV m^{-1}, and that fields above 25 kV m^{-1} produced annoying sensations (Clairmont *et al* 1989).

- they induce surface charges on conducting objects. Currents may pass through grounded people in contact with such objects. Field strengths greater than approximately 5–7 kV m^{-1} can produce a wide variety of safety hazards such as shock reactions associated with spark discharges and contact currents from ungrounded conductors within the field.

Care should be taken to eliminate ungrounded metallic objects, or to ground such objects. There is a paucity of information on the health effects of exposure to static electric fields when the confounding factors of surface charge are eliminated (NRPB 1993). The effects of exposure to static electric and magnetic fields on circadian rhythms have been investigated. Male volunteers were isolated for periods of between 3 and 8 weeks in a self-contained underground exposure chamber; the daily cycle of activity and body temperature was unaffected by exposure to static electric fields of 600 V m^{-1} (Wever 1970).

4.1.2 Magnetic fields

A number of possible magnetic field interaction mechanisms have been proposed. For example, magnetic fields are known to affect organic chemical reactions which involve a radical pair as an intermediate stage, possibly increasing free radical formation at low flux densities (McLauchlan 1992), although the biological significance of this effect is yet to be established. The natural occurrence of ferromagnetic magnetite (Fe_3O_4) crystals in animal tissue has been implicated in the migratory behaviour of fish and birds; however, the significance of their occurrence in human brain tissue (Kirschvink *et al* 1992) is not clear. Movement in a static magnetic field will, however, induce electric fields and currents which may be implicated in sensory responses observed in volunteer experiments (NRPB 1993).

Acute responses

There is no direct experimental evidence of any acute, adverse effect on human health due to short-term exposure to static magnetic fields of up to about 2 T (UNEP/WHO/IRPA 1987, NRPB 1993). The exposure of volunteers to fields of up to 0.15 T for up to 1 h did not induce a change in the performance of a number of mental tasks. Body temperature, heart rate and blood pressure are unaffected by acute exposure to fields up to about 1.5 T; one study reported a slight drop in heart rate in humans exposed to 2 T.

Experiments with mammals, including two primate species, confirm a lack of effect on cardiac function of exposure to fields of less than about 2 T (UNEP/WHO/IRPA 1987, NRPB 1993). In particular, there were no significant changes in heart rate or arterial blood pressure in monkeys exposed to 1.5 T, although this exposure was sufficient to generate measurable electric potentials arising from blood flow. The evidence from carefully conducted experiments is that circadian rhythms and the spontaneous and learned behaviour of rodents are unaffected by chronic exposure at about 1.5 T. This result is consistent with a lack of effect of exposure to up to about 2 T on isolated nerve preparations and of exposure to 1.5 T on the electro-retinogram response of cats and squirrel monkeys.

Effects on behaviour and cardiac function from exposure to much higher magnetic flux densities than 2 T cannot be ruled out. It has been reported that people working around a 4 T magnet experienced vertigo and nausea during rapid head movement (Schenck *et al* 1992). These responses did not occur in subjects lying stationary within the field. In addition, sensations of flickering light, magnetic phosphenes, were noted during rapid movement of the eyes. These can be induced by weak electric currents, which suggests that both responses may have originated from weak electric currents induced by head or eye movement in a large static magnetic field. The experimental evidence for an effect of static magnetic fields above 2 T on the nervous system of animals is equivocal. The performance of learned tasks by squirrel monkeys was reduced during exposure to static fields in excess of about 5 T (de Lorge 1979). Changes in the electrical activity recorded from the brains of squirrel monkeys during exposure to between 2 and 9 T have been found (Beischer and Knepton 1966), although it has been suggested that these responses could be artifacts, possibly due to muscle activity. A temporary increase in sinus arrhythmia and decrease in heart rate were observed in squirrel monkeys which were acutely exposed to fields mainly between 4 and 7 T (Beischer and Knepton 1964), although a threshold could not be identified.

Chronic exposure

There is little experimental information describing possible effects of chronic exposure. So far, however, no long-term effects have become apparent (UNEP/WHO/IRPA 1987, NRPB 1993).

Experimentally induced changes in the orientation of static magnetic fields at flux densities approximately equivalent to that of the Earth's magnetic field have been reported to affect the nocturnal melatonin levels in rodents; more intense fields (of up to 2 T) had no effect on circulating stress hormone levels. Chronic exposure to fields of up to 2 T had no reliable effect on body weight, haematological profile, or on the few immunological responses investigated. The animal data also indicate that implantation and development of the embryo and fetus are unlikely to be affected by exposure for the whole period of gestation to static magnetic fields of up to at least 1 T.

There is no convincing evidence that static magnetic fields are mutagenic (UNEP/WHO/IRPA 1987, NRPB 1993). Exposure to fields of up to about 1 T does not affect dominant lethal frequency in male germ cells *in vivo*, nor the frequency of chromosome aberrations and sister chromatid exchanges in cells exposed *in vivo* or *in vitro*. A lack of mutagenicity suggests that exposure is not capable of initiating carcinogenesis. Tumour progression and tumour promotion also seem to be unaffected by exposure to static fields of at least 1 T.

4.2 Time varying electric and magnetic fields of frequencies less than 100 kHz

Among the many general reviews describing the biological effects of exposure to time varying electromagnetic fields of frequencies less than 100 kHz are UNEP/WHO/IRPA (1984, 1987), Grandolfo *et al*, (1985), Bernhardt (1988), Anderson (1991), Sienkiewicz *et al* (1991, 1993), ORAU (1992), and NRPB (1993). The specific effects on cells and cellular systems have recently been reviewed by Cridland (1993).

Electric currents applied directly to the body can stimulate peripheral nerve and muscle tissue, and such effects can prove fatal if breathing is inhibited or ventricular fibrillation induced. There is an established literature describing these effects in relation to electric current passing through the body as a result of contact with a live conductor.

Exposure to time varying electric fields can result in perception effects due to electric charge on the surface of the body. ELF electric fields external to the body induce electric fields and currents within the body as a result of the variation with time of the induced surface charge density; the induced current density generally decreases as the body cross-section decreases and depends on the electrical properties of tissue. ELF magnetic fields induce closed loops of circulating electric currents in such a way that the largest current densities tend to be induced in peripheral tissues, decreasing in magnitude towards the centre of the body. It is well established that these induced currents can affect the normal function of electrically excitable nerve and muscle cells and it has been suggested that the most frequently observed effects of exposure relate to various subtle effects on the brain and nervous system (Anderson 1991). The reported effects on circadian rhythms and melatonin secretion, on pregnancy outcome and on carcinogenesis appear more equivocal.

4.2.1 Electric fields – studies on volunteers

Relatively few laboratory studies on the effects of electric field exposure on humans have been carried out. The available experimental evidence suggests that, apart from the perception of the field resulting from induced surface charge, the effects of exposure to fields of up to 20 kV m^{-1} are few and subtle, and may be masked by normal biological variation.

ELF electric fields can be perceived because of the field-induced vibration of body hair, or the occurrence of spark discharges on contact with clothes or grounded objects. An amplitude of vibration of several millimetres for the hairs of the forearm exposed to a 50 Hz field of 50 kV m^{-1} has been reported. The threshold for perception by hair vibration shows wide individual variation:

10% of exposed subjects have detection thresholds of less than $10–15$ kV m^{-1} at 50–60 Hz, while only 5% are able to detect fields as low as $3–5$ kV m^{-1} (UNEP/WHO/IRPA 1984, Bernhardt 1988). The threshold depends on the relative positions of the head, trunk and limbs, simply as a consequence of the different perturbations of the incident field. Although these effects are not considered to be a hazard, hair vibration and tingling if sustained can become an annoyance.

ELF electric fields, interact with biological bodies through electric charges induced on ungrounded metallic objects, such as cars, trucks, cranes, wires and fences (Zaffanella and Deno 1978). Two types of interaction may occur:

- a spark discharge between the object and the person touching the object;

- the passage of current to ground through a person coming into contact with such an object; the magnitude of the current depends on the total charge on the object and on the person's impedance to ground. This charge, in turn, depends on the frequency and electric field strength, the object geometry and its capacitance.

Above a certain threshold, the current to ground is perceived by the person as a tingling or prickling sensation in the finger or hand touching the charged object, for frequencies below about 100 kHz, and as heat at higher frequencies. A severe shock can be experienced at levels much higher than threshold. The threshold currents depend on frequency and on surface of contact area. The threshold for effects (perception, shock, etc) are generally higher for men than for women and children, though there are also individual differences (UNEP/WHO/IRPA 1993).

All effects due to induced charges on objects are defined below in order of increasing severity:

- Perception - The person is just able to detect the stimulus. There is a difference in the current perception threshold for touch and grip contact.

- Annoyance - The person would consider the sensation to be a mild irritant, if it were to occur repeatedly.

- Startle - The sensation is severe enough to cause a startle response in the person.

The remaining reactions apply only to contact with alternating currents at frequencies below 100 kHz.

- Let-go - A person cannot let go of a gripped conductor as long as the stimulus persists, because of uncontrollable muscle contraction. If a person is exposed to prolonged currents, somewhat above the let-go level, through the chest, breathing becomes difficult and, eventually, the person may become exhausted.

- Respiratory tetanus - A person is unable to breath as long as the stimulus is applied, owing to the contraction of the muscles responsible for breathing.

- Fibrillation - The heart is unable to pump blood around the body as the stimulation causes uncoordinated, asynchronous contractions of the heart.

Threshold currents for the occurrence of the above effects are given in table 4.1. Thresholds for perception and pain (well below the let-go) were evaluated for nearly 200 men and 200 women and also estimated for 10 year old children (Chatterjee *et al* 1986). Thresholds are lower for finger contact than for grasping contact. The stimuli in both cases are tingling/prickling at frequencies below about 100 kHz and heat/warmth at higher frequencies.

TABLE 4.1 **Threshold currents (mA) for various effects at frequencies ranging from 50/60 Hz to 300 kHz (experimental data for men, women and children)***

Effect	Subject	Threshold current (mA) at various frequencies						
		50/60 Hz	300 Hz	1000 Hz	10 kHz	30 kHz	100 kHz	300 kHz
Touch perception	men	0.36	(0.47)	(0.70)	4	15	40	40
(finger contact)	women	0.24	(0.31)	(0.53)	3.2	12	35	35
	children	0.18	0.24	0.40	2.5	8	25	25
Grip perception	men	1.1	1.3	2.2	15	50	300	300
	women	0.7	0.9	1.5	10	35	200	200
	children	0.55	0.65	1.1	9	30	150	150
Shock, not painful	men	1.8	(2.3)	(3.2)	17(10)	(25)	(25)	
(grasping contact)	women	1.2	1.5	2.1	11	16.7	16.7	
	children	0.9	1.1	1.6	8.5	12.5	12.5	
Pain	men	(1.8)	(2.4)	(3.3)	10	30	55	50
(finger contact)	women	1.2	1.6	2.2	6.5	23	47	45
	children	0.9	1.2	1.6	6	18	33	30
Shock, painful;	men	9	(11.7)	(16.2)	55	(126)	(126)	
muscle control (let-	women	6	7.8	10.8	37	84	84	
go-threshold for	children	4.5	5.9	8.1	27	63	63	
0.5% population)								
Painful shock	men	16	18	24	75(88)	(224)	(224)	
let-go threshold	women	10.5	12	16	50	150	150	
	children	8	9	12	37	112	112	
Severe shock,	men	23	(30)	(41)	94(126)	(320)	(320)	
breathing difficulty	women	15	20	27	63	214	214	
	children	12	15	20.5	47	160	160	

*From Dalziel 1954a,b, Deno 1974, Guy and Chou 1982, Guy 1985, Chatterjee *et al* 1986). Data in brackets were calculated by using the frequency factors for perception thresholds and for pain and let-go thresholds, given in IEC Publication 479-1 (IEC 1984). Data in italics were calculated by assuming thresholds for women two-thirds of that for men and thresholds for children one-half of that for men (IEEE 1978, Guy 1985).

Currents flowing from an object to ground through a person who has touched that object can be reduced if shoes are worn (Chatterjee *et al* 1986). Electric charge induced on various objects and, therefore, contact currents for people, can be calculated for a known electric field strength. Results of such calculations are in table 4.2 for men, women and children in finger contact with different vehicles.

Another interaction that may occur at lower frequencies is a transient discharge, which occurs between a person and charged object either by direct contact or through an air gap.

Of greater biological significance may be the occurrence of capacitive spark discharges (microshocks) which are generated when two objects of different potential come into close proximity and the electric breakdown field strength of the air is exceeded (Reilly 1978, Larkin and Reilly 1984, Tenforde and Kaune 1987). These spark discharges will continue as long as the air gap and the potential difference is maintained. The current flows across a very small area of skin and results in a high current density which may be perceptible, irritating or painful. Exposed people may demonstrate stress reactions in the presence of repeated spark discharges with increased nervousness and inability to continue work.

TABLE 4.2 Electric field strength for person to vehicle currents and short circuit body current for persons exposed to electric fields with feet grounded (data from table 4.1, Deno 1974, Guy 1985, Chatterjee et al 1986)

Effect	Subject	Field strength (kV m^{-1})								
		50 Hz	60 Hz	300 Hz	1000 Hz	10 kHz	30 kHz	100 kHz	300 kHz	1 MHz
Touch perception	men	5.0	4.0	1.1	0.54	0.30	0.36	0.45	0.20	0.17
(finger contact, car)	children	2.5	2.0	0.54	0.27	0.19	0.27	0.28	0.15	0.12
Pain (finger contact, car)	men	24	20.4	5.4	2.2	0.75	0.85	0.55	0.30	0.18
	women	16	13.6	3.6	1.5	-	-	-	-	-
	children	12	10.2	2.7	1.1	0.48	0.55	0.38	0.18	0.15
Pain (finger contact, bus)	children	3-5	-	-	-	0.15	0.2	0.18	0.13	0.12

The threshold for the perception of spark discharges by 10% of a group of volunteers close to an earthed object has been reported to be 0.6 to 1.5 kV m^{-1} at 50 to 60 Hz, with a similarly defined threshold for annoyance of 2 to 3.5 kV m^{-1} (Bernhardt 1988). Sensitivity appears to depend on such factors as skin hydration, body location and skin temperature.

Results are available from extensive 50 Hz laboratory tests on volunteers where the exposure conditions and control groups seem to be well defined. The laboratory tests include field exposure times from 3 h to 1 week and field strengths of up to 20 kV m^{-1} (Hauf 1985, Kühne 1980). The variables examined were reaction time to visual and auditory stimulation, psychological factors, ECG, EEG, blood pressure, pulse frequency, body temperature, blood status, biochemical parameters of blood and urine, enzymes and metabolic factors. No significant changes were found.

Recent studies have reported that exposure to a weak fields appears to affect the gross electrical activity of the brain, although the functional significance of these results is not known (Sienkiewicz *et al* 1993). Field-induced changes in neuronal excitability within the central nervous system could be responsible for producing observable changes in behaviour. However, exposure to 60 Hz electric fields of up to 30 kV m^{-1}, or magnetic fields of up to 1 mT, does not appear to reduce the performance of learned tasks by rodents or non-human primates, and other effects on behaviour observed during exposure of animals to an electric field, such as transitory changes in arousal or activity in rodents, or in the social behaviour of baboons are more likely the result of stress caused by perception of the field by cutaneous stimulation.

4.2.2 Magnetic fields – studies on volunteers

There is little experimental evidence to suggest that time varying magnetic fields can affect human physiology or behaviour at the intensities occurring in the environment or in the home.

At frequencies below approximately 100 kHz, interactions of time varying magnetic fields with biological systems and potential hazards can be considered in terms of induced currents and current densities. The use of induced current densities, however, is only appropriate for the assessment of acute, immediate effects, while it may have some limitations for the complete evaluation of long-term effects. The waveform of the electromagnetic field is an important factor to be considered in the response of biological systems. Peak instantaneous field strengths appear to be important in considering nerve and muscle cell stimulation and for perturbing cell functions. Generally, for frequencies above 100 to 1000 Hz, the thresholds for effects increase with frequency, up to frequencies where thermal effects dominate.

The ability of people to perceive 50 or 60 Hz magnetic fields has been studied by several groups. An obvious difficulty in these studies and in studies on field effects on behaviour is that the electromagnet used for exposure inevitably generates noise and vibrations, due to the forces acting on the windings; this may act as a conspicuous cue. The generation of fields for more than about 10 mT leads to a high noise level unless appropriate precautions are taken. A well designed study found that, in the absence of other cues, magnetic fields at intensities comparable to those normally associated with occupational exposures cannot be perceived by people (Tucker and Schmitt 1978). More than 200 subjects were exposed to a 60 Hz field at a magnetic flux density of 0.75 or 1.5 mT in an isolation chamber designed specifically to remove incidental stimuli that could indicate the presence of the field.

A number of examinations have been performed using volunteers. Many have investigated effects on the visual system and it is well known that magnetic fields can induce faint flickering sensations in the periphery of the visual field, the magnetophosphenes. They were first reported in

1896 (D'Arsonval 1896) and have subsequently been confirmed and further investigated. The sensation has been described as "a faint flickering illumination, colourless, or of a slight bluish tint perceived over the whole region of vision". The effect was increased by increasing the field intensity. The threshold for this effect has been quantified. Volunteers were exposed to a magnetic field, generated by an electromagnet placed close to their temples, at frequencies from 10 to 45 Hz and at field intensities between 0 and 40 mT. The sensitivity thresholds were found to be frequency dependent with a minimum threshold (maximum sensitivity) of approximately 10 mT at 20 Hz, although threshold values as low as 2 mT have been quoted, rising at lower and higher frequencies. The threshold was also found to be modulated by the luminance level and spectral composition of the ambient light and, following dark adaptation, was increased with increasing time in darkness.

The response is thought to result from the effects of induced electric current on retinal cells. The threshold current density at 20 Hz is estimated to be 10 mA m^{-2}. The same response can be induced by electric currents directly applied via electrodes attached to the head. However, it is not clear which cells within the retina are affected by induced current; the visual receptors (rods and cones) are exquisitely sensitive, but only to optical radiation. There are a large number of different nerve cells within the retina which have an integrative function, reflecting the embryological derivation of the retina as an outgrowth of the brain. Most of these cells (except the ganglion cells which form the optic nerve) exhibit slowly varying potentials which sum the effects of different inputs and will be intrinsically sensitive to weak electric fields and currents. If these cells are affected, then the implication is that nerve cells within the central nervous system (which also have integrative functions) will also be susceptible to electric field and currents of a similar magnitude.

Stimulation of peripheral nerves and muscles by magnetically induced electric currents in tissue requires exposure to more rapidly varying magnetic fields, usually generated as one or a few short pulses. McRobbie and Foster (1984) describe a threshold of perception of about 2 10^3 T s^{-1} in volunteers whose forearms were exposed to a damped sinusoidal magnetic field (2 to 3 cycles of a period equal to 0.3 ms). The current density induced in the peripheral tissue of the forearms were calculated to be several A m^{-2}. In addition, direct stimulation of the motor cortex using very short pulses (< 1 ms) applied directly above the motor cortex has been used to selectively excite voluntary muscles.

Following the development of clinical magnetic resonance imaging (MRI) diagnostic techniques, patients are routinely exposed during examination to intense (up to several mT), time-varying longitudinal and transverse gradient magnetic fields, pulsed at frequencies below about 10 kHz. Recently, experiments have been carried out using volunteers in order to identify thresholds for peripheral nerve stimulation. Small, involuntary muscular twitches of the nose, and sometimes of the lower back and thigh, were reported. Threshold values depend on the orientation of the magnetic field relative to the body and have been estimated to range between about 25 and 60 T s^{-1}, the lower values corresponding to transverse magnetic field orientations.

The exposure of volunteers for several hours to 45 to 60 Hz fields of up to 5 mT had no effect on a number of clinical and physiological tests, including haematology and blood biochemistry, ECG, heart rate, blood pressure and body temperature; elevated triglyceride levels were ascribed to other, confounding factors (UNEP/WHO/IRPA 1987). However, the performance of a short-term memory task was improved following exposure at only 0.1 mT whilst that of an arithmetic task was impaired; the authors noted that this did not indicate a general impairment of cognitive function. Volunteers exposed to intense ELF magnetic fields (up to 100 mT) at frequencies between 5 and 50 Hz have reported "indisposition and headaches" during exposure above 60 mT. Changes were also recorded in the visually evoked potential response, although visual acuity itself was apparently unaffected. A lack of effects was reported on other physiological parameters, such as blood pressure, ECG, EEG, and body temperature.

Electric currents are generated within the tissues and organs of the body by the electrical activity of nerve and muscles tissues. These endogenous currents, which may reach 1 mA m^{-2} in the brain (a level generated in peripheral tissue by exposure to 50/60 Hz magnetic fields of about 0.5 mT), are considered unlikely to affect function and other tissue.

4.2.3 Effects on circadian rhythms and melatonin secretion

Various investigations have shown that power frequency electric (and magnetic) may affect circadian rhythms in primates and rodents and a number of studies have reported specific field-induced changes of pineal gland function. It has been suggested (Wilson *et al* 1989, Stevens *et al* 1992) that the effect on serum melatonin concentration could contribute to an increased risk of cancer via direct and indirect effects on mammary tumour cell growth, although there is as yet no direct experimental evidence of this effect. The results of the initial experiments using power frequency electric fields (see Wilson and Anderson 1990, Reiter 1992) indicated that the exposure of rats to electric fields above a threshold of 0.2 to 2 kV m^{-1} for at least 21 days severely reduced the normal nocturnal peak in synthesis and secretion of melatonin by the pineal gland. However, several preliminary studies (see Sienkiewicz *et al* 1993) have not reported such robust or obvious field-dependent effects in a variety of animals, including rats, primates and ewe lambs, and the existence for any association must remain tentative (Goldberg and Creasey 1991).

Exposure to power frequency magnetic fields has also been reported to affect pineal function (see Reiter 1992, Sienkiewicz *et al* 1993). Acute exposure to a pulsed static field at 40 μT or chronic exposure to a 60 Hz field at 1 mT has been reported to depress nocturnal pineal melatonin levels in rats: in both cases, intermittent exposure appeared to cause a greater effect than continuous exposure. However, very rapidly pulsed static fields failed to cause any change in pineal function. A reduction in urinary levels of a metabolite of melatonin has been reported in some volunteers following night-time exposure to a very weak (0.4 to 0.7 μT) 60 Hz magnetic field from an electric blanket (Wilson *et al* 1989). However, these results were highly variable, and were only found in 7 out of 28 subjects. The robustness of these effects and their implications for human health are not clear at present.

4.2.4 Reproductive and developmental effects

There is some concern about the possible adverse effects of exposure to electromagnetic fields on the development of the embryo and fetus. Whilst, however, the results of experimental investigations of electromagnetic field effects on chick development remain equivocal, the evidence suggests that such exposure has no established effect on mammalian development (Chernoff *et al* 1992, Brent *et al* 1993, NRPB 1994).

Several large, carefully conducted electric field studies in which rodents or miniature swine were exposed to 60 Hz electric fields as high as 130 kV m^{-1} did not reveal any adverse effects on male fertility or on reproductive performance, nor any consistent effects on development (for example, Sikov *et al* 1987, Rommereim *et al* 1990). Some statistically significant changes in malformation incidence were reported but were either not reproducible in replicated experiments or the incidence varied widely between different sham groups but was, overall, of a similar range to that in the exposed groups. However, one unreplicated study reported specific changes in the operant behaviour of adult rats who had been exposed throughout gestation to combined 60 Hz electric and magnetic fields up to 30 kV m^{-1} and 0.1 mT (Salzinger *et al* 1990).

A number of magnetic field studies have reported that the development of chick embryos can be adversely affected by exposure to low level, pulsed or sinusoidal ELF fields at 10–1000 Hz. In contrast, other studies have reported a lack of statistically significant effects after the exposure of chick embryos to pulsed, sawtooth or sinusoidal magnetic fields at frequencies of 50 Hz to 20 kHz. A large scale, carefully conducted study (Berman *et al* 1990) which attempted to define the response of chick embryos to low level, low frequency fields using six replicate experiments failed to provide clear evidence of a response; overall, the results indicated a statistically significant increase in the incidence of malformations in the exposed group, but there were significant differences between the results of the replicate studies.

The results of studies with mammals appear less equivocal; in general, no well established developmental effects have been found (Chernoff *et al* 1992, Brent *et al* 1993, NRPB 1994). For example, a non-significant increase in pre-implantation and post-implantation survival following the exposure of rats for the first 20 days of gestation to a 50 Hz magnetic field of about 37 μT peak-to-peak flux density (Huuskonen *et al* 1993). There was no effect on the incidence of external, visceral or skeletal abnormalities when the data were analysed by litter, although an increase was reported in the incidence of minor skeletal variants; however, this is a relatively common finding in teratological assays. A lack of adverse effects on embryo and fetal development following prenatal exposure throughout gestation to a 20 mT, 50 Hz magnetic field has also been reported (Kowalczuk *et al* 1994); no significant effects on pre-implantation or post-implantation survival or on the incidence of visceral or skeletal abnormalities were found.

The postnatal sequelae of prenatal exposure to magnetic fields have been investigated in a number of studies; few positive effects have been reported (NRPB 1994). For example, the exposure of mice to a 50 Hz magnetic field at 20 mT throughout gestation did not affect postnatal growth or various developmental indices, including the time to eye opening, nor affect locomotory or exploratory behaviour of juveniles or adults (Sienkiewicz *et al* 1994); but an earlier appearance of the righting reflex and a transitory decrease in motor co-ordination was noted. Other studies, however, have reported various changes in the time to appearance of the righting reflex and of eye opening and have reported variable and transitory effects on postnatal weight. It would seem likely that these different, uncorroborated findings are the result of chance or uncontrolled experimental variables.

Several studies have investigated the effects of very low frequency (VLF) fields, typical of visual display units (VDUs), on development in mammals. Variable effects on post-implantation survival and the incidence of external abnormalities have been reported in pregnant mice exposed to 20 kHz sawtooth magnetic fields at peak flux densities of 1 μT or 15 μT. In general, however, other well conducted large scale studies report a lack of effect of VLF exposure (Chernoff *et al* 1992, Brent *et al* 1993, NRPB 1994). For example, no effects on post-implantation survival or on the incidence of external or internal malformations or skeletal defects have been observed in mice exposed to 20 kHz sawtooth fields of up to 200 μT (peak to peak) for the first 18 days of gestation (Wiley *et al* 1992). Similarly, no consistent developmental effects have been observed in rats exposed for the first 20 days of gestation to 20 kHz magnetic fields of 15 μT (peak-to-peak) flux density (Huuskonen *et al* 1993).

4.2.5 Carcinogenesis

Carcinogenesis is generally believed to involve at least three stages: initiation, usually involving genetic mutation of one or more cells; promotion, involving multiplication and accumulation of damaged cells; and progression, the accumulation of further genetic abnormalities, resulting in increased malignancy.

Initiation

There is no convincing experimental evidence that ELF electromagnetic fields cause genetic damage (McCann *et al* 1993, Murphy *et al* 1993) and it is therefore extremely unlikely that they could have any effect on the initiation of cancer. In support of this conclusion, one large scale animal study (Yasui *et al* 1992) of rats exposed to power frequency magnetic fields for about 2 years found no effect on spontaneous tumour frequency. It is more generally accepted that if ELF fields do affect carcinogenesis it is likely to be at the level of promotion. However, the experimental evidence for this is weak and inconclusive (Sienkiewicz *et al* 1993).

Promotion

The possibility that electromagnetic fields might act in a promotional capacity has been investigated at the cellular and subcellular levels, principally by exploring the possibility that cell signalling pathways may be affected leading to increased cellular proliferation. The earliest signal transduction events which have been investigated with respect to ELF fields are ion fluxes. A number of studies of transmembrane Na^+,K^+-ATPases have indicated changes in both ATP hydrolysis and ion pumping in response to ELF electric fields, although there are considerable differences in the responses seen in different studies (see Tsong 1992, Blank 1992). A number of cell signalling pathways produce transient increases in the intracellular concentration of free Ca^{2+}; several studies have sought to investigate the possibility that electromagnetic fields act to stimulate calcium ion movements, and thereby influence these pathways. For example, studies by Walleczek and Liburdy (1990) reported that a 22 mT, 60 Hz magnetic field increased the influx of Ca^{2+} which resulted from stimulation with the mitogen Concanavalin A. Further experiments indicated that the influx of calcium depended on the induced electric field and demonstrated that the direct application of a similar electric field produced the same effect (Liburdy 1992). Preliminary reports from other groups (Walleczek *et al* 1992, Lyle *et al* 1992) also using fluorescent indicators to monitor intracellular ion concentrations have suggested that a human leukaemia cell line may be unresponsive at similar field strengths, but may respond, albeit differently, when exposed to 50 Hz electric fields of about 5 V m^{-1}. These effects do not, however, establish a promotional effect of electric or magnetic field exposure.

Medium- and long-term regulation of cell function is mediated principally at the level of transcription, which is itself controlled mainly through modulation of the rate of transcriptional initiation. A number of studies examining the effects of low frequency fields on transcription have been published in recent years, although most have originated from just one laboratory. Early studies reported increased RNA synthesis at multiple sites on several chromosomes in cultured fly salivary glands, and have been reviewed elsewhere (Goodman and Henderson 1991, Cridland 1993). Other studies (see Sienkiewicz *et al* 1993) have reported that exposure of a lymphoblastoid cell line to a pulsed magnetic field induced a short-term increase in the synthesis of both total and messenger RNA. The exposure of leukaemic cells to power frequency magnetic fields produced a temporally similar, though quantitatively smaller, increase in total RNA synthesis. However, the significance of these reported short-term increases in gross transcription is difficult to assess. Clear and unequivocal evidence for effects on the transcription of specific genes, particularly those known to be important for regulating cellular behaviour would be of far greater importance. Unfortunately the evidence for this is much less convincing; in particular, the absence of proper controls and the failure to use appropriate techniques renders the data extremely difficult to interpret (Cridland 1993, Sienkiewicz *et al* 1993).

One of the most important endpoints for cell signalling is modulation of the rate of cellular proliferation, a process which may have important implications for human health. It is now widely accepted that most tumour promoting chemicals act to stimulate proliferation, whilst there is evidence that increased proliferation may be tumorigenic even in the absence of exposure to specific initiators. In general, however, the existing literature relating to the effects of electromagnetic field exposure on cellular proliferation reports many apparently conflicting results including direct stimulation and inhibition in addition to both positive and negative modulation of mitogen action (Cridland 1993). These apparent inconsistencies may reflect differences in exposure parameters or the responses of different cell types.

Tumour promotion has also been examined directly using animal carcinogenesis models. One model which has been used is the development of mammary gland tumours induced by a chemical initiator (DMBA) in female rats. This was reported to be only marginally affected by chronic exposure to 60 Hz electric fields at 40 kV m^{-1} (Leung *et al* 1988) or 50 Hz magnetic fields at up to 30 mT (Mevissen *et al* 1993). A well established model for chemical promoters examines tumour induction in mouse skin painted with a chemical initiator. Chronic exposure to a 60 Hz field at 2 mT (McLean *et al* 1991) or to a 50 Hz field at either 50 or 500 μT (Rannug *et al* 1993) did not affect DMBA-induced skin tumours. These results strongly suggest that ELF fields do not act as classical tumour promoters. In contrast, Beniashvili *et al* (1991) reported that repeated exposure of rats to a 50 Hz magnetic field (20 μT) for 3 h daily enhanced the induction of mammary tumours by the chemical carcinogen nitrosomethyl urea. Both the number of tumours per tumour bearing rat, and the number of rats with tumours were increased; in addition, the tumours in the exposed group appeared significantly earlier than those in the control group. However, the significance of this report is weakened by the incomplete description of the experimental protocol. Löscher *et al* (1993) also reported an increased incidence and an earlier appearance of mammary tumours in DMBA treated rats exposed to 50 Hz magnetic fields of 100 μT, although the number of tumours per tumour bearing rat was unaffected. These studies are not definitive, but there is clearly scope for further investigation.

Co-promotion

There is some preliminary evidence to suggest that magnetic fields may act as a tumour co-promoter by enhancing the inhibitory effect of a known tumour promoter on gap junctional communication, thereby releasing the inhibitory effect of adjacent normal cells on the growth of premalignant cells. A study by Cain *et al* (1992), using untransformed mouse fibroblasts to inhibit the growth of transformed C3H10T½ cells reported that simultaneous exposure to a 100 μT, 60 Hz field enhanced a chemical promoter (TPA) -induced inhibition of transformed cell growth. In a whole animal study (Stuchly *et al* 1992), mice exposed to a 2 mT, 60 Hz magnetic field following initiation of skin tumours with DMBA and subsequent weekly TPA application developed tumours more rapidly than those treated with DMBA and TPA alone, although final numbers of tumours per animal were not affected. Importantly, both groups have recently reported a failure to successfully replicate these studies.

Tumour progression

Exposure to magnetic fields does not appear to affect the progression of tumours although possible effects on tumour progression have been examined directly in few studies (see NRPB 1993). One study did not find any effect of exposure to 60 Hz fields of up to 500 μT on the progression of leukaemia in mice which had been injected with leukaemic cells. Similarly, the incidence of leukaemia in a strain of leukaemia-prone mice was unaffected by periodic exposure to a 6 mT magnetic field pulsed at either 12 or 460 Hz.

4.2.6 Immune system responses

Changes in immune function could also result in effects on tumour progression. However, exposure of animals to magnetic fields does not appear to result in any significant inhibition of immune response (Sienkiewicz *et al* 1993). Exposure for 7 days to a 50 Hz magnetic field at 20 mT did not affect bone marrow stem and progenitor cells numbers or either total or differential white blood cell counts in mice (Lorimore *et al* 1990). Mice exposed to a 2 mT power frequency magnetic field after treatment with a subthreshold dose of the carcinogen DMBA showed no effect on mononuclear cell counts, on natural killer cell activities in spleen and blood, or on spleen size (McLean *et al* 1991).

4.2.7 Frequency/amplitude specific effects

There is evidence of biological responses to low level ELF electric fields (less than 100 V m^{-1}) at frequencies between about 1 and 400 Hz (NRPB 1993); such effects include altered mobility of calcium ions in chick and cat brain tissue, changes in neuronal firing patterns in rodents and in electrical activity of the brain and operant behaviour of non-human primates. Both frequency and amplitude windows for such effects have been reported. In addition, changes in enzyme activity showed amplitude windows in response to directly applied 60 Hz electric currents. Extension of the work which identified changes in the exchange of ^{45}Ca^{2+} in isolated chick brain in response to very weak electromagnetic fields led to the proposal of resonant interactions in which it has been suggested that the local geomagnetic field plays a role in transduction (for example, Liboff 1987). It has been reported that combined static and time varying magnetic fields can affect calcium-dependent movement of marine micro-organisms or the uptake of radio-labelled calcium ions when the ELF frequency is at an appropriate resonance frequency for calcium ions, although replication has proved difficult. In addition, other recent experiments report that the performance of an operant task and a spatial memory task are impaired in rats only during exposure to these particular conditions.

4.3 Electromagnetic fields and radiation of frequencies between 100 kHz and 300 GHz

This section provides an overview of the biological effects relevant to considerations of the health and safety of people exposed to radiofrequency and microwave radiations (Grandolfo *et al* 1983, Saunders *et al* 1991, NRPB 1993, UNEP/WHO/IRPA 1993). As frequencies increase above 100 kHz, well-established biological effects can be related to the thermal load or the degree of heating resulting from field interactions with electrically charged (or polarised) ions or molecules. Water is a particularly strong absorber of microwave radiation, and so tissue with a high water content will show a greater power absorption per unit mass (specific energy absorption rate, or SAR) than tissue with a low water content. The majority of biological responses to exposure to radiofrequency and microwave radiation are consistent with heating or frank rises in tissue temperature.

A large number of animal experiments have been carried out, but the data are unevenly distributed within the very broad range of frequencies covered by this section, the majority being at a few commonly used frequencies such as 915 MHz or 2.45 GHz, while fewer experiments have been carried out at lower frequencies.

Studies of isolated (*in vitro*) components of a biological system offer possible insights into the mechanisms of radiofrequency action. *In vitro* systems are simple, allowing biological variables to be controlled and subtle effects to be identified without being masked by the homeostatic responses of the whole organism.

The results of *in vitro* studies conducted so far suggest that the cell membrane is a site of interaction of RF fields and that alterations in membrane permeability may result from athermal interactions, particularly in response to amplitude-modulated fields as well changes in membrane cation fluxes, changes in the activity of certain enzymes, and suppression of some immune responses (Franceschetti *et al* 1989).

A substantial body of data exists describing biological responses to amplitude-modulated RF or microwave fields at SARs too low to involve any response to heating. In some studies, effects have been reported after exposure at SARs of less than 0.01 W kg^{-1}, occurring within modulation frequency windows (usually between 1 and 100 Hz) and sometimes within power density windows; similar results have been reported at frequencies within the voice frequency (VF, 300 Hz to 3 kHz). Some of these responses have been difficult to confirm, and their physiological consequences are not clear.

While *in vitro* studies are important in determining the mechanisms of interaction and identifying appropriate biological endpoints and exposure conditions to be tested in whole animals, they cannot serve as a basis for health risk assessment in humans. *In vivo* studies are necessary in order to evaluate the integrated response of various systems of the body that serve to maintain homeostatis, the condition necessary for the proper functioning of the body. Three bodily systems can be identified as of particular importance in this respect: the nervous, endocrine, and immune systems. The coordinated interdependent interaction of these systems in response to chemical and physical stimuli provides a great capacity for adaptation and compensation in response to changes in environmental or internal body conditions.

Moreover, some individual tissues may be particularly sensitive to the heating effects of radiofrequency and microwave radiation, mainly because of their lack of blood supply, and consequent limited cooling ability. From this point of view, the lens of the eye and the testis can be potentially regarded as critical organs.

4.3.1   Studies on volunteers

These experimental studies provide the most valuable and reliable information, because of their controlled character. In particular, exposure levels and conditions can be well controlled, so that thresholds for effects, if any, may be identified.

An effect which has been investigated in some detail on volunteers is warmth perception, because this is a valid indicator of a substantial heat deposition which in turn may lead to a number of thermally related effects.

A number of studies have shown that cutaneous perception of heat arises only at frequencies of the order of several gigahertz or more, ie, when the wavelength is comparable with the thickness of the skin, where thermal sensors are located. That means that in the lower frequency RF range, and in particular in the whole and partial body resonance regions, internal organs may undergo temperature increase and possibly damage without any sensation of warmth by the individual during exposure.

On the other hand, it has been observed that the threshold for pain corresponds to a surface temperature of the skin of about 46°C, much above the threshold (42°C) for cellular damages. In conclusion, volunteers studies on warmth perception or sensation of pain demonstrate that these effects are not reliable indicators of potentially hazardous exposures.

The auditory sensation induced by pulsed RF/MW fields has also been widely investigated. Controlled experiments have been performed in order to clarify the mechanism for this effect and the role of radiation parameters, such as power density, energy density per pulse, pulse width, etc. The results indicate that the phenomenon is due to thermoelastic waves induced in the head, and that the process is most effective at frequencies between 6 and 9 GHz.

4.3.2   Nervous system

Results of early studies (in anaesthetised rats) suggested that the blood-brain barrier was possibly susceptible to RF field exposure. However, later work indicated that these responses may have been confounded by a number of factors including the use of anaesthetics.

Pulsed RF exposures appear to have various effects on the nervous system, the data supporting the hypothesis that low level RF fields may act as mild nonspecific stressors, such as heat and noise. Exposure to very high peak power pulses is reported to suppress startle reflex and evoke body movements in conscious mice.

High levels of RF radiation significantly decrease the latency of evoked potentials if spinal or thalamic temperatures are raised by several degrees celsius. Exposure to low levels of pulsed or continuous microwave or radiofrequency radiation at SARs as low as 0.46 W kg^{-1} can affect neurotransmitter metabolism and the concentration of receptors involved in stress and anxiety responses in different parts of the brain. Exposure to very low levels of amplitude-modulated RF and microwave radiation has been reported to alter brain activity (measured using EEG) and to affect calcium ion mobility in the cortex. Exposure to microwave radiation at levels sufficient to raise body temperature has been shown by several authors to affect the distribution of barbiturate drugs.

4.3.3   Endocrine system

The endocrine responses to acute microwave exposure are generally consistent with the acute responses to nonspecific stressors, such as heat, or with changes in metabolism caused by hyperthermia. Several papers report that plasma corticosterone or cortisol levels are significantly enhanced by exposure above a threshold level which decreases with longer durations of exposure. This response seems to be mediated by the hypothalamus and is amplitude modulated by the circadian rhythm of cortisol or corticosterone levels.

No effects on the endocrine system were seen in a lifetime study on rats exposed between 2 and 27 months of age at SARs of up to 0.4 W kg^{-1}.

4.3.4   Haematopoietic and immune systems

In a large number of studies, haematological effects have been found in animals exposed to radiofrequency radiation, mainly when a significant rise in body temperature has been observed. Few effects have been reported in the absence of a detectable increase in temperature, while thermal responses have not been established at all. No consistent changes were found in erythrocyte, leucocyte, or differential leucocyte cell count in rats exposed pre- and post-natally to RF fields.

RF exposure has been reported to affect various components of the immune system. Whilst both stimulatory and inhibitory responses have been reported, these have been mostly transient in nature and usually attributable to thermal stress.

A lifetime exposure study in which rats were exposed to up to 0.4 W kg^{-1} between 2 and 27 months of age did not reveal any effects on haematological or immunological parameters, except for a transient change in the number and response of B- and T-lymphocytes to specific mitogens after a 13-month exposure.

4.3.5   Ocular effects

The lens of the eye is potentially sensitive to radiofrequency exposure, because it lacks a blood supply and so has a reduced ability to dissipate heat compared with other tissues. In addition, the fibres that make up the bulk of the lens have only a limited capacity for repair and tend to accumulate damage and cellular debris.

In most experimental work on the microwave induction of cataracts, the rabbit has been used as the experimental animal model, because the dimensions of its eye approach those of the human eye. The microwave frequencies most effective in inducing cataracts lie between about 1 and 10 GHz. Below about 1 GHz, the dimensions of the orbit-eye combination are too small to result in local field concentration.   Above about 10 GHz, penetration decreases and power absorption becomes increasingly restricted to the superficial tissue. The threshold power density to produce a cataract is approximately 1500 W m^{-2} for 1 to 3 hours, corresponding to an SAR of about 100 to 140 W kg^{-1}.

The few experiments which have investigated the effects of chronic, whole-body exposure of rabbits to power densities up to 100 W m^{-2} (ie, well below the threshold value) reported a lack of effect on the lens.

4.3.6   Cardiovascular system

The responses of the intact cardiovascular system to RF and microwave exposures appear to be consistent with responses to conventional heating. An increase in cardiac output, heart rate and blood pressure, coupled with a decrease in peripheral resistance, has been reported in rabbits exposed to SARs estimated at 10 to 15 W kg^{-1}, raising body temperatures by 0.5°C, and in anaesthetised rats exposed at levels which increased body temperature by about 3.5°C. Chronic exposure of rats at SARs of between 0.3 and 2.5 W kg^{-1} did not affect heart rate and weight.

4.3.7   Behaviour

A variety of behavioural changes have been reported in recent years in animals exposed to RF and microwave radiation. Research in this area can be divided arbitrarily into two categories: short-term and long-term exposures. Short-term exposures are generally used to identify health risks associated with intense exposure levels and ensuing thermal effects, which overwhelm the natural thermoregulatory capability of the experimental animal.   Long-term experiments are used to investigate the cumulative effects of exposure over weeks and months at relatively low power density levels, in order to prevent a deviation of body temperature from the normal range.

Short-term exposures may result in behavioural changes. The minimum colonic temperature rise associated with significant behavioural changes in rodents and non-human primates is close to 1°C. Under normal ambient conditions the SAR associated with this temperature rise is approximately

87

4 W kg^{-1}; it is less under higher ambient temperature and relative humidity and is dependent on frequency.

The behavioural changes include alterations in trained performance, motor behaviour, and behavioural thermoregulation. Exposures can result in thermal stress reactions and in less time spent in the electromagnetic field.

Long-term exposures to radiation at low power density levels also lead to behavioural changes, including alterations in trained performance and motor behaviour, although in this case colonic temperature rise is not expected. These changes are frequency dependent and occur at SARs of 0.9 to 2 W kg^{-1} at 915 MHz, 1.5 to 3.6 W kg^{-1} at 1.3 GHz, and 0.4 to 0.7 W kg^{-1} at 2.45 GHz. The differences resulting from radiation frequency are explained in terms of the heterogeneity of energy absorption in the rodent body.

4.3.8   Reproduction and development

Most of the studies on reproduction and development in small mammals exposed to radiofrequency radiation have shown effects that can be related to a temperature rise, and can be produced by thermal stress alone.

It is well known that in many species of mammals the development of male germ cells can be adversely affected by an increase of testicular temperatures (usually maintained 3 to 4°C below body temperature). Temporary sterility was found in male rats exposed at an SAR of about 6 W kg-1 for 4 h per day for 20 days.

Exposure to high levels of RF will induce significant rises in maternal body temperature, and result in deformities or defects in the offspring. From a review of the teratogenic effects of exposure to RF, principally in mice and rats, the conclusion can be drawn that intense exposures that result in significant maternal heating can result in reduced fetal mass, specific abnormalities, and in increased embryo and fetal losses.

4.3.9   Genetic effects

Experimental evidence suggests that acute or long-term RF and microwave exposures do not result in an increase in chromosome aberration frequency, when temperatures are maintained within physiological limits. One study reported an increased frequency of cytogenetic effects in mice exposed long-term at SARs of 0.05 to 20 W kg^{-1}, but it was not successfully replicated.

In general, all data suggest that the only exposures that are potentially mutagenic are those at high radiofrequency power densities, which result in a substantial increase in temperature.

4.3.10   Cancer-related studies

The evidence suggests that RF and microwave radiation is not mutagenic and is therefore unlikely to initiate cancer; however, very few cancer-related studies are available (NRPB 1992). The evidence for a co-carcinogenic effect or an effect on tumour promotion or progression is not convincing, and these issues deserve further investigation.

One large-scale study reported an increase in the number of primary malignancies in 100 rats exposed for most of their lives to microwave radiation at SARs of up to 0.4 W kg^{-1} when compared to sham-exposed animals, but not when compared to other published frequencies for the same strain of animals; there are other inconsistencies in the data. The chronic exposure of mice at much higher SARs (up to 8 W kg^{-1}), possibly causing some localised heating, resulted in an increase in the progression of spontaneous or chemically induced tumours. Studies of mouse C3H10T1/2 cells exposed to microwave radiation at 0.1 to 4.4 W kg^{-1} followed by TPA treatment revealed a dose-dependent increase in neoplastic transformation rate; however, the results from these chromosomally abnormal cells can not be directly extrapolated to carcinogenesis *in vivo*.

4.3.11   Auditory perception

Short pulses of microwave energy impinging on heads of animals and humans have been shown to elicit auditory responses. The response is believed to stem from thermoelastic expansion of tissue in the head, which absorbed the pulsed microwave energy. More specifically, when a microwave pulse impinges on the head, the absorbed energy is converted into heat, which produces a small but rapid rise in temperature. This temperature rise, occurring in a very short time, generates rapid thermoelastic expansion of tissue in the head, resulting in a pressure wave detected by hair cells in the cochlea of the inner ear.

Threshold specific energy densities for pulses shorter than 30 ms were reported as 10 to 16 mJ kg^{-1} for cats and 0.9 to 1.8 mJ kg^{-1} for rats.

4.3.12   Indirect effects

In the frequency range between 100 kHz and 100 MHz, RF shocks and burns can result from touching ungrounded metal objects that have been charged by the field or from the charged body coming into contact with a grounded metal object. These effects are called *indirect effects*, resulting from an interaction between electromagnetic fields or radiation, an external object such as a metallic structure, and the human body.

The current flowing into the body has a strong dependence on the size of the object, and is a function of both the RF field and the impedance of the object to the ground. Sufficiently high current densities for contact burns can be attained in RF fields that are too low to cause direct heating or stimulation. Simple electric measurements, however, are sufficient to establish the risk, and precautionary measures may be instituted. In general, RF burns will not occur from current point contact of 50 mA or less. Generally, thresholds are lower for finger contact than for grasping contact.

On the basis of experiments on 50 volunteers at frequencies between 2 and 20 MHz, the maximum tolerable current that can be drawn through finger contact is 200 mA (Rogers 1977).

4.4   Optical radiation

4.4.1   Ultraviolet radiation

The skin, the outer barrier of the human body with the environment, is a highly dynamic organ capable of passive and active protection responses to many deleterious environmental attacks and agents such as chemicals, radiations, bacterial infections, temperature, mechanical stress. The outer part of the skin is the epidermis, a rather uniform layer (150 to 180 μm thick) comprising a series of cell layers. The epidermis is attached to the underlying layer, the dermis, by the basal lamina and a monolayer of proliferative cells, the basal layer.

Optical radiation impinging upon the skin can be reflected, absorbed or scattered. Scattering consists of a change of direction of propagation and leads either to absorption or to back reflection. These three processes are wavelength dependent and determine the penetration of the radiation into the skin. For normally incident radiation the reflectance of the skin varies between 5 and 8% but becomes progressively higher at larger angles of incidence. The biological effects due to the absorbed fraction result directly or indirectly from two basic mechanisms of absorption: photochemical reactions and heating or a combination of the two. Photochemical reactions are those that initiate with the absorption of a photon by a specific molecule or chromophore and produce reactive atoms or molecules which combine with other atoms or molecules. The amount of energy deposited by a photon and its spatial distribution as it traverses the skin influence the biological response.

Photons of ultraviolet radiation in the UVC spectral region penetrate rather poorly into the skin because of the strong absorption displayed by nucleic acids, proteins and urocanic acid. UVB radiation penetrates deeper and therefore photons interact with chromophores located in the epidermis and in the upper part of the dermis. UVA radiation has the greatest penetration into the skin and therefore structural and functional biological effects induced by photons of this spectral region may also affect nerve fibres, nerve endings, blood cells and peripheral blood vessels.

A small fraction of the radiation produces photochemical reactions, most is absorbed by skin pigments and rapidly converted into heat.

The intrinsic effects of UVR on human skin depend on its sensitivity which in turn is strictly related to its constitutive features and adaptive responses. Humans exhibit different reactions and the same radiant exposure can produce a different degree of response due to the intrinsic sensitivity of the skin of the exposed individual. In Caucasians (white population) four different phototypes or skin types, which are genetically determined, can be defined. Skin colour, UV reactions, and values of UVB minimal erythemal dose (MED) corresponding to the four different phototypes are summarised in table 4.3.

TABLE 4.3   Phototypes or skin types (Pathak and Fanselow 1983)

Skin type	Unexposed skin colour	MED-UVB J m⁻²	Sensitivity to UVR	Sunburn and pigment response
I	White	150–300	Very sensitive	Always burns easily never tans
II	White	250–350	Very sensitive	Always burns easily tans minimally
III	White	300–500	Sensitive	Burns moderately, tans gradually - light brown
IV	Light brown	450–500	Moderately sensitive	Burns minimally, always tans well - moderate brown

Acute reactions on the skin

Sunburn is a well-known response of human skin to UVR. It is easily detectable in fair-skinned individuals and appears as a reddening of the skin (erythema), a visible indication of peripheral vasodilatation due to the inflammation response triggered by UV damage. Erythema appears a few hours after a radiant exposure exceeding the threshold value for each phototype and reaches its maximum 12–24 hours after the irradiation and gradually fades over 3–4 days. Severe forms of erythema may induce fever and result in blistering and oedema. The erythemal response is rather important because it is recognised as a subjective sensitivity index for the deleterious effects of UVR on the skin. Many variables, such as spectral distribution of source emission, skin type and pigmentation, affect the radiant exposure required to induce erythema. The relative effectiveness of UVR of different wavelengths to induce erythema can be expressed by means of an action spectrum which allows the evaluation of the erythemal effectiveness of a broad-band optical source. The erythemogenic properties of UVC, UVB and UVA are linearly additive and the law of reciprocity holds over orders of magnitude of irradiances. Several erythema action spectra have been proposed.

The reference action spectrum proposed by McKinlay and Diffey (1987) is used widely and incorporated in standards and guidelines, figure 4.1.

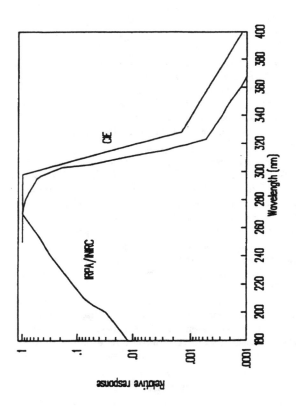

FIGURE 4.1   Reference action spectrum for UV-induced erythema in human skin (CIE) and the IRPA/INIRC relative effectiveness spectrum for protection of the eyes and the skin. (McKinlay and Diffey 1987, IRPA/INIRC 1989).

Minimum erythemal dose (MED)

The degree of redness of the skin produced by a known radiant exposure is difficult to quantify because of the subjective evaluation of the observer. It seems more appropriate to describe the phenomenon in terms of presence or absence of redness. The MED defines the threshold radiant exposure required to induce a detectable erythema. This non physical quantity depends on subjective skin sensitivity and when expressed in terms of effective radiant exposure, according to the spectrum for erythema, ranges between 50 and 400 J_{eff} m^{-2}. For practical radiation protection purposes a MED corresponding to a radiant exposure of between 200 and 300 J m^{-2} is often used. This range of values corresponds to the threshold for the erythema (MED) in a lightly pigmented, unexposed Caucasian subject.

Natural mechanism of defence of the skin

Human skin reacts to the harmful effects of UVR by activating several responses which result in a significant increase in protection against UVR.

The most effective basic mechanisms of defence against UVR developed by the human skin are the following.

- Keratinisation of the external layers of the epidermis to form a compact horny layer, the so-called stratum corneum whose scattering and absorbing properties attenuate the radiation transmitted to the viable and dividing cells. This is the basic constitutive role of the horny layer. The adaptive response consists in the epidermis thickening process due to stimulated proliferation of basal layer keratinocytes triggered by UVR (hyperplasia of epidermis). Skin thickening leads to increased UV skin tolerance and is a very important adaptive response in lightly pigmented people.

- Skin pigmentation, a gene regulated process involving epidermal melanocytes in melanin synthesis. The constitutive pigmentation is the baseline skin colour of a person in the absence of exposure to UVR. Adaptive pigmentation (tan) is a protective response that reduces injury from subsequent exposures and results from increased melanin production stimulated by UVR. Constitutive and adaptive pigmentation can provide significant protection against harmful effects of UVR. In whites two different types of melanin are produced: eumelanin (black melanin) and phaeomelanin (red or yellowish melanin). In principle all people produce a mixture of the two but phototype I people produces mainly phaeomelanin and phototype IV people eumelanin. The synthesized melanin molecules are concentrated into a matrix of a specific cytoplasmic membrane-limited organelle, the melanosome. In whites two different melanosomes are found; eumelanosomes and phaeomelanosomes. Phaeomelanosomes, typically produced by red-haired clear skin subjects, are small, irregularly shaped melanosomes intrinsically susceptible to enzymatic degradation. The phaeomelanins they carry are photolabile and do not exhibit effective protection properties. This particular feature explains why phototype I people do not tan.

- Upon UV irradiation phototypes III and IV people produce a progressively greater amount of eumelanin which accumulates on the external layers of the epidermis. These people exhibit a positive defence reaction and tan well. Melanins are basically the only pigments within the human skin that change the level of transmitted UVR. The photoprotective action of melanins peaks at 330 nm, drops off rather quickly at shorter wavelengths and slowly decrease at longer wavelengths. The relative effectiveness of radiation of different wavelengths in inducing skin tanning shows that UVB radiation is orders of magnitude more effective than UVA (Parrish *et al* 1982, Ortel and Gange 1992) The important practical consequence in cosmetics, for example, is that UVA sources have to have substantially higher irradiances compared with UVB appliances, to induce pigmentation in a reasonable, practical exposure time. The melanogenesis in fair skinned individuals lasts for several days because delayed tanning is a multistep process involving melanocyte stimulation and synthesis of melanins, and transfer of melanosomes from melanocytes to keratinocytes.

- Urocanic acid, the enzymatic product of histidine deamination, is thought to act as a filter in the epidermis and the horny layer. This endogenous sunscreen absorbs UVR through a *cis-trans* isomerisation and oxidation reaction. Urocanic acid synthesis increases for weeks following UV exposure. Profuse sweating may also be considered as a sort of photoprotective reaction since it results in the accumulation of urocanic acid on the skin.

- Beta carotene, a natural biopigment present in many vegetables and fruits such as carrots, tomatoes and oranges, has been shown to be a systemic photoprotective agent. This molecule, which displays its maximum absorption in the visible spectral region does not act as a filter. In the dermal and subcutaneous tissue its main role is to act as a quencher against free radicals and highly reactive oxygen species produced by UVR which are associated with cutaneous photoaging, skin cancer and other skin disorders.

- Damage to cellular targets such as DNA, proteins and membranes induced by longer wave UV radiation (UVA) is primarily due to oxidative processes. The most important antioxidants in the epidermis and dermis which can act as radical scavengers or hydrogen donors are: the tri-peptide glutathione, glutathione-peroxidase, glutathione-reductase and superoxide dismutase. All these antioxidants prevent damage to membrane lipids and to epidermal and dermal proteins, by inactivating the oxidising species generated by UVR.

- It is generally assumed that DNA is the primary target of UVR. Damage includes single-strand breaks, DNA-crosslinks and cyclobutane type pyrimidine dimers. The biological relevance of these lesions is directly related to the capacity of the cell to repair the damage. Cells of the human skin have developed an efficient mechanism for dealing with such damage. Pyrimidine dimers are rapidly removed and repaired by an error-free excision repair mechanism.

Long-term effects of UVR on the skin
UV radiation can induce basically two types of long-term effects on the skin, photoaging and cancer:

Skin photoaging Photoaging superimposes upon normal ageing of the skin as a consequence of repeated exposure to UVR. Such damage is related to cumulative radiant exposure and leads to premature aging of the skin. The cellular and molecular mechanisms involved in skin photoaging are not well understood but the predisposition of photoaged skin to develop skin cancers suggests that the basis of the cumulative damage to the epidermis and dermis may be identified in gene mutation and damage. Photoaging degeneration occurs on both epidermal and dermal tissues and results in reduced elasticity, increased skin fragility and other histological changes of connective tissues.

Skin cancer UV related skin cancers occur mainly in white populations. Many descriptive data and epidemiologic studies indicate over the past three decades a substantial rise in the incidence of skin cancer (Magnus 1991). There are two types of skin cancer related to UV exposure: (a) skin carcinomas or non-melanocytic skin cancer (NMSC) originating from epidermal keratinocytes, and

(b) cutaneous malignant melanoma (MM) resulting from neoplastic transformation of epidermal melanocytes.

Several mechanisms have been proposed to correlate skin carcinogenesis to UVR exposure. However the picture is not well understood since photoinduced carcinogenesis is a complex multistep process involving local and systemic responses in which many genetic and epigenetic factors play a crucial role. Many controlled experiments in animals have been carried out in several laboratories to understand skin cancer photogenesis, the wavelength dependency of UV carcinogenesis and the incidence relationship with radiant exposure. Important results have been obtained but many qualitative and quantitative aspects of the phenomenon still need to be clarified.

(a)   *Skin carcinomas* Non-melanocytic skin cancers include basal cell carcinomas (BCC) and squamous cell carcinomas (SCC). They stem from keratinocytes of the epidermis: the BCC from basal layer keratinocytes and the SCC from differentiated keratinocytes of the spinous layer. Basal and squamous cell carcinomas are generally more common in males than females, and the head and the neck, which are regularly exposed to radiation, are the most common body sites.

These two observations suggest a relationship with exposure to UVR. Epidemiological data on SCC show a clear relationship with the UV radiant exposure whereas the risk of BCC does not hold with a model simply related to the total exposure. Outdoor work as well as recreational outdoor activities show a positive association with skin carcinomas and there is also evidence of an inverse gradient of risk with latitude. Phototype, hair and eye pigmentation, propensity to burn rather than tan and other host factors such as solar keratoses, history of sunburns and solar lentigines show a positive relationship with basal and squamous cell carcinomas (Kricker *et al* 1991). Basal cell carcinomas grow fairly slowly and hardly ever metastasise. Squamous cell carcinomas grow faster than BCC and the risk of metastasis increases with the size of tumoral lesion. NMSC is by far the most common form of skin cancer among whites. The overall mortality in developed countries is very low and is mainly due to SCC although this cancer represents only around 20% of the total number of NMSC.

(b)   *Cutaneous melanoma* Cutaneous malignant melanoma occurs primarily in light-skinned populations. This disease is by far the most serious form of skin cancer.

Response of immune system to UVR

Experiments on the transplantation of highly antigenic murine carcinomas indicate that they are not rejected following exposure to UVR of the recipient mice. Human data from renal transplant patients who receive prolonged immunosuppressive have also shown that UVR has important effects on the immune system resulting in an increased host susceptibility to skin cancer and certain infection diseases (Kripke 1974, Greene *et al* 1981). Studies on mechanisms related to UVR-induced immune suppression have focused on the effects on the epidermal Langerhans' cells (antigen presenting cells) and on the keratinocyte-cytokines system and their interaction with T lymphocytes that together constitute the peripheral arm of the immune system.

The Langerhans' cell is effective at stimulating T cells and is one of the most important targets of UVR in the skin. UVR alters the morphology of Langerhans' cells and impairs their ability to present tumour antigen. This photoinduced effect has important consequences on the pathogenesis of UVR induced skin cancer and may also be relevant to viral infections and viral replication.

The keratinocytes, the largest cell population of the epidermis, release a family of soluble proteins known as cytokines. It is known that UVR influences the synthesis and release of these molecules. The altered modulation of cytokines can result in an altered functional activity of cells involved in tissue healing, inflammation and tumour initiation.

These effects have been observed also in non-irradiated sites, suggesting a possible role of UVR in systemic immune suppression.

Phototoxic and photoallergic reactions

Photosensitivity consists of adverse cutaneous reactions induced by photoproducts or reactive intermediates formed during photodegradation of some chemical substances. Photosensitising compounds may have endogenous or exogenous origin and reach the skin by contact or through topical application or systemic administration. Skin dermatitis, which includes both acute reactions and/or chronic lesions, occurs through two different processes: phototoxicity and photoallergy. Phototoxic reactions are an altered response of the skin, independent of immunologic mechanisms, related to radiation exposure and to radiation-induced phototoxins. Theoretically phototoxic reactions can occur in all individuals provided the radiant exposure, the wavelength of UVR and concentration of the photosensitiser are appropriate. Photoallergy is a cell mediated immune response transferred through lymphoid cells, leading to an altered capacity of the skin to react to optical radiation alone or in the presence of a photosensitiser.

The formation of an antigen is the main step of a photoallergic reaction. Upon the absorption of a photon the photosensitizing molecule can form either another stable compound or be excited to a highly reactive state. In both cases the photoinduced intermediates bind to a protein and form the antigen. Photoallergy reactions are confined mostly to the exposed areas of the skin and include immediate urticaria, delayed papular or an eczematous responses similar to contact dermatitis. Photoallergy response is strongly dependent on subjective sensitivity and other host factors such as pigmentation. Many cosmetics, plant extracts, drugs and industrial substances are known to induce phototoxic or photoallergic reaction. Lists of these compounds are available in some countries (for example, U.S. Department of Health and Human Services 1990).

UVR and the eye

The eye is an approximately spherical organ coated by an outer layer transparent on the front and opaque posteriorly called, respectively, the cornea and the sclera. Within the eyeball the optic media include successively the aqueous humour, the lens, the vitreous humour and the retina.

The optic media can be considered in terms of successive spectral filters each one absorbing in a particular spectral region, according to its particular chemical composition, thus preventing the transmission of radiation of specific wavelengths to the next structure. The human cornea transmits radiation of wavelengths as short as 300 nm and the lens absorbs nearly all UVR with wavelengths shorter than about 380–400 nm.

Cataracts Opacities in the normal transparent lens of the eye which impair visible light transmittance to the retina are called cataracts. There are several different types of cataracts and different causal factors. Epidemiological data show an increased risk for some types in relation to sunlight exposure. Cellular and molecular aging of the lens epithelium and fibres lead to cataract formation.

This phenomenon occurs naturally but it can be exacerbated by exposure to UVB radiation through mechanisms involving either direct damage to proteins of the lens or photoxidative reactions by singlet oxygen to proteins and membranes. Cataracts occur mostly in older people. In addition to natural aging they can result either from long-term low level exposure, acute high level doses or a combination of the two (Pitts *et al* 1986). It is extremely difficult to determine any retrospective reconstruction of the lifetime exposure to sunlight and UVB due to large factors of uncertainty.

Photokeratitis The cornea is the anterior outer surface of the eye. It is a moist surface washed by a tear film and richly supplied with nerve endings. Acute exposures to UVC and UVB radiations cause corneal damage and a well-known short-term acute response called photokeratitis (and photoconjunctivitis when referred to the conjunctiva). The superficial inflammatory reaction is accompanied by pain, lacrimation and a very uncomfortable sensation of grains of sand in the eye.

The action spectrum for photokeratitis peaks between 265 and 275 nm and UVA radiation is orders of magnitude less efficient in causing this effect. The geometry of ocular exposure is fundamental in defining the irradiance on and the absorption of the cornea. In conditions of overhead exposure from the midday sun up to 50% of solar UVR incident upon the cornea is reflected because of the geometry of the head and the eyes. When the geometry of exposure changes because of ground reflection, a typical example being a fresh snow field, the threshold for corneal damage becomes significantly lower. Photokeratitis and photoconjunctivitis are fortunately transient and reversible at or around threshold exposures and disappear within a few days.

4.4.2   Effects of non-laser optical radiation on the retina

In the visible and infrared A spectral regions (400–1400 nm), the eye is virtually transparent and the radiation penetrates to the retina, the sensitive neural tissue where the photoreceptors are located. This spectral region is termed the retinal hazard region. The combined refractive powers of the cornea and to a lesser extent the lens amplify the irradiance on the retina with respect to that incident on the cornea and such energy concentration can be potentially harmful (Marshall 1987). Surgical removal of the lens following cataract and the implant of plastic lenses not designed to absorb UVA can result in significant higher UVR exposure to the retina of the unprotected aphakic eye. Exposures to long wave visible radiation and near infrared (IRA) elevating the temperature of the retina about 10 to 20°C above the normal value can result in irreversible denaturation of proteins and thermal damage. Exposures to irradiances far below the threshold for thermal damages in the spectral region 380 to 500 nm, can induce photochemical related damage (so called blue-light damage). This damage due to the action of photoinduced oxidising species involves injury to both photoreceptors and retinal pigment epithelium (Ham *et al* 1986, Massof *et al* 1986).

Ascorbic acid, alpha tocopherol, superoxide dismutase, glutathione reductase and peroxidase and catalase are the natural defence systems that protect the retina from photochemical damages. This system gradually fades with age and by contrast the damage gradually accumulates over years to produce pathologic conditions. Decreased visual acuity and molecular degeneration are two pathological findings associated with photochemical damage to the retina.

Exposure of the human eye to IRR may result in adverse effects in eye lids, cornea, iris, lens and retina mostly related to heat produced by radiation absorption. The predominant mechanism of damage is thermal denaturation of biomolecules and biostructures. Damage to the cornea induced by IRR exposure from extended sources is rather unlikely because of the rapid pain reaction followed by lid closure. When the blink reflex is not sufficient to prevent damages, opacification of the cornea can occur.

Since the 18th Century it has been known that long-term exposure to IRR could lead to lens opacification, known as IRR cataract. Such pathology occurred frequently among glass blowers and steel industry workers. Nowadays, legal restrictions, worker's information and training, and the extensive use of personal protective equipment have considerably reduced the risk of IRR cataract.

4.4.3   Effects of laser radiation

Laser radiation injuries Lasers are sources of highly directional beams of spatially and temporally coherent optical radiation. Because of the small angular divergence of the beam, ranging from fractions of a milliradian to few milliradians, high power is emitted within a small solid angle.

The radiance of such a source can be extremely high. A laser having a power output of few mW is many orders of magnitude brighter than all the other sources of optical radiation and is even brighter than the sun. It is known that the maximum retinal irradiance which defines the concentration of power into a small area of the retina irradiated by a source, depends only on the radiance of the source itself. Lasers are therefore capable of producing very high irradiances in the retina.

This feature leads to several important positive applications of lasers but also to a great potential for causing injury in particular on the eye.

Generally in the past laser exposures did not represent an environmental hazard to the general public. Lasers were mostly used in confined or restricted areas, industries, universities, hospitals, military applications. In the last two decades, however, an increasing number of laser sources, mainly emitting visible radiation, have been used for display and entertainments purposes, in cosmetics and beauty applications, for illumination of art exhibits and holographic public displays. All these applications pose the problem of exposing the general public to levels which may exceed maximum permissible exposures. In practice the risk of incurring injury can be avoided with adequate controls and procedures for use.

Biological effects of laser radiation Biological effects of laser radiation depend on certain characteristics of the beam, which in turn influence the probability of injury, and on the intrinsic structure, function and sensitivity of biological tissues hit by the beam.

The main parameters of the laser beam are:

- The wavelength, which influences the depth of penetration into tissues and the absorption by specific cromophores.
- The temporal emission characteristics, which affect the temporal exposure and in turn the mechanism of interaction between laser radiation and biological tissues. Pulse duration and pulse repetition rate strongly influence the response. If the same amount of energy is delivered to the target over a shorter period of time, for example, nanoseconds instead of milliseconds, the potential for tissue damage becomes greater.
- The radiant exposure which is the quantity of energy across the beam impinging on the tissues surface in a given time.

The biological response depends also on the intrinsic properties of tissues. Reflection, scattering and absorption phenomena are related to the molecular composition and microscopic structure of tissues. They are wavelength dependent and determine how laser radiation is spatially distributed at the tissue surface and in depth.

Ocular effects The eye is the most critical target for laser exposure because of the inherent transparence and susceptibility of its structures and because of its focusing properties in the retinal hazard region.

The retinal image for intrabeam viewing by a relaxed or unaccommodated human eye corresponds approximately to that of a lens of 17 mm focal length.

Collimated laser beams impinging on the eye produce small images on the retina, from the diffraction limit, 10 to 20 μm diameter, for a beam divergence less than a milliradian to about 200 μm diameter for a divergence of 10 milliradians. The amount of energy entering the eye is controlled by the iris. Depending upon the luminance of the environment the diameter of the pupil can range from 2 to 8 mm. The pupillary area is proportional to the square of its diameter, thus 16 times more energy can enter the eye when the pupil diameter widens from 2 to 8 mm. Pupil diameter affects also the probability that a small laser beam can enter the eye. The optical gain (magnification factor) which defines the gain of irradiance of the eye from the cornea to the retina for a point source is influenced by pupil diameter. An optical gain of up to 10^5 is quite normal for pupil diameters from 4 to 8 mm. The obvious consequence of so high an amplification is that a corneal irradiance of 1 W cm^{-2} will become 100 kW cm^{-2} irradiance on the retina. The possible damage to the retina due to extremely high irradiances can range from a retinal burn in the periphery of the fundus, to severe damage to the macula with loss of visual acuity, to very severe damage resulting in massive haemorrhaging and rupture of retinal tissue. The degree and the nature of injury to the retina depends in a complex fashion on various physical parameters including the radiation wavelength, irradiance, exposure time and image size.

In the retinal hazard spectral region exposures which are safe for the retina exclude possible damage to other parts of the eye. When the exposure is considered safe for the eye any adverse biological effect to other parts of the human body can be excluded.

Physical mechanism of injury Thermal injury requires that the radiant energy is at a wavelength greater than about 400 nm and when absorbed increases the temperature of the exposed tissue, above the normal value during a certain time. The same level of damage can be produced by different combinations of temperature elevation and time of exposure.

Thermal damage varies significantly with the image size. Heat transfer to adjacent unexposed tissues from small images, such as a collimated laser beam focused on the retina, is more effective in reducing the increase of temperature than it is from larger images.

Laser pulses ranging from 1 picosecond to 1 microsecond produce very high temperature gradients. The absorption of optical radiation is partially converted into heat and partially in thermomechanical or acoustic effects. Depending upon radiant exposure the vaporisation or even the rupture and vaporisation of exposed tissues may occur.

Several biological effects originate from photochemical reactions rather than through a heat mediated mechanism. Photochemical effects predominate at a wavelength lower than 550 nm and pulse durations longer than about 1 s since each interacting photon should provide a sufficient quantum energy to trigger a photochemical reaction.

A typical photochemical effect is the so called blue-light damage to the retina. In principle a constant radiant exposure should induce the same photochemical effect over quite different exposure times. In the 400 nm to 550 nm spectral region photochemical and thermal mechanisms overlap and their interaction can mutually enhance biological effects.

4.5   Summary

4.5.1   Static and slowly time varying fields

The few experimental studies that have been carried out on the biological effects of static electric fields provide no evidence to suggest the existence of any adverse effect on human health. For most people, the annoying perception of surface electric charge, acting directly on the surface of the body, will not occur during exposure to static electric field strengths of less than about 25 kV m^{-1}.

There is no direct experimental evidence of any acute adverse effect on human health from exposure to static magnetic fields of up to 2 T. There is less information on the effects of chronic exposure but no long-term effects have become apparent.

4.5.2   Time varying electric and magnetic fields of frequencies less than 100 kHz

It is well established that exposure to electric and magnetic fields results in the induction of electric fields and currents in biological tissues, and may result in a variety of nervous system responses. A threshold current density of 10 mA m^{-2} between 10 Hz and 1 kHz can be conservatively estimated for weak effects on central nervous system activity. Few studies have been performed with human volunteers, and the most consistent response other than the appearance of retinal visual stimulation (magnetophosphenes) appears to be the minor reduction in heart rate observed immediately during or after exposure to a combined electric and magnetic field. The small magnitude and transitory nature of this effect, however, does not suggest a health risk.

Most biological studies suggest that exposure to low frequency electric and magnetic fields does not have any significant effects on mammalian development. Similarly, there is no persuasive evidence that ELF electromagnetic fields are able to influence any of the accepted stages in carcinogenesis, the results of animal studies have been essentially negative. Effects on initiation are extremely unlikely suggesting that if there is an effect it will be at the level of promotion or progression. Here, the evidence remains confused with no clearly reproducible effects apparent.

Time varying fields can be perceived because of the field-induced surface charge via vibration of body hair or the occurrence of spark discharges on contact with clothes. Mean perception thresholds are about 10 to 20 kV m^{-1} for 50 Hz, while only 5% of people are able to detect fields as low as 3 to 5 kV m^{-1}.

The perception and annoyance thresholds for perceiving contract currents or spark discharges (microshocks) are relatively low. The annoyance threshold for the perception of spark discharges has been reported to be 2 to 3.5 kV m^{-1} at 50/60 Hz. There is a frequency dependence for this effect.

4.5.3   Electromagnetic fields and radiation of frequencies between 100 kHz and 300 GHz

Many of the biological effects of acute exposure to electromagnetic fields are consistent with responses to induced heating, resulting in rises in tissue or body temperature of about 1°C or more. Most responses have been reported at SARs above about 1 to 2 W kg^{-1} in different animal species exposed under various environmental conditions. These animal (particularly primate) data indicate the types of responses that are likely to occur in humans subjected to a sufficient heat load. However, direct quantitative extrapolation to humans is difficult given species differences in responses in general, and in thermoregulatory ability in particular.

The most sensitive animal responses to heat loads are thermoregulatory adjustments, such as reduced metabolic heat production and vasodilation, with thresholds ranging between about 0.5 and 5 W kg^{-1}, depending on environmental conditions. However, these reactions form part of the natural repertoire of thermoregulatory responses that serve to maintain normal body temperatures. Transient effects seen in exposed animals which are consistent with responses to increases in body temperature of 1°C or more (and/or SARs in excess of about 2 W kg^{-1} in primates and rats) include reduced performance of learned tasks and increased plasma corticosteroid levels.

Most animal data indicate that implantation and the development of the embryo and fetus are unlikely to be affected by exposures which increase maternal body temperature by less than 1°C.

Above these temperatures, adverse effects, such as growth retardation and post-natal changes in behaviour may occur, with more severe effects occurring at higher maternal temperatures.

Most animal data suggest that RF exposure low enough to keep body temperature within the normal physiological range is not mutagenic. Such exposure will not result in somatic mutation nor in hereditary effects.

There is much less information describing the effects of chronic low-level exposure. So far, however, it is not apparent that there are any long-term effects which can result from exposures below thermally significant levels.

The possibility that exposure to RF fields might influence the process of carcinogenesis is of particular concern. So far, there is no definite evidence that irradiation does have an effect. Many experimental data indicate that RF fields are not mutagenic, and so they are unlikely to act as initiators of carcinogenesis; the few studies carried out have looked mostly for evidence of an enhancement of the effect of a known carcinogen.

4.5.4   Optical radiation

Because of the limited penetration of optical radiation in tissue, the adverse health effects of optical radiation on the body are limited mainly to the skin and the eyes, although systemic effects are also possible. The effects are strongly wavelength dependent, with photochemical ones dominating at shorter wavelengths, and especially in the ultraviolet region, and thermal ones at longer wavelengths, principally in the infrared region. Pulsed laser radiation produces additional effects characterised by very rapid absorption of energy by tissue.

Effects on human skin include acute UVR-induced erythema, skin cancers, photoaging and heating as well as UVR-induced localised responses affecting the immune function of the skin. Effects on the eye include acute UVR-induced corneal (photokeratitis) and conjunctival effects, UVR-induced and thermal-induced changes in the lens possibly leading to cataract, and photochemical, thermal and thermoacoustic effects on the retina.

Exposure of the general public is dominated by solar radiation even though the contribution from artificial sources has increased significantly over the past 30 years or so. Solar radiation exposure is clearly implicated in the increased incidence of skin cancer. A quantitative evaluation of risk for the induction of skin cancer requires a dose-response relationship to be established. The dose-response relationship and the carcinogenic potential of UVR for the induction of non-melanoma skin cancer in mice have been established but there are as yet few data relevant to the spectral effectiveness of UVR for the induction of malignant melanoma.

UVR can induce local or systemic responses by affecting the immunological function of the skin. The skin contains Langerhans' cells, keratinocytes and T cells, the cellular components of the peripheral immune system. Experimental work on animals has shown that low level exposure to UVR impairs the immune surveillance system at the site of the exposure and higher levels of exposure suppress the immune system elsewhere also. These effects could have important implications with respect to human health.

Cataract is a multifactorial disease related to the natural aging process. There is evidence that ultraviolet radiation can play a role in its onset and temporal progression. Long-term exposure to IRR can also lead to lens opacification (infrared cataract).

Optical radiation in the spectral region approximately 400 to 1400 nm is transmitted through the anterior media of the eye and focused, principally by air/corneal interface, onto the retina. Photochemical retinal injury can result from sufficiently high exposure to visible radiation with a strong blue-light component. The degree of injury is related to the total energy absorbed. Thermal retinal lesions may occur as the result of exposure to very high radiance sources such as a high power laser.

References

Allen, S G, Bernhardt, J H, Driscoll, C M H, Grandolfo, M, Mariutti, G F, Matthes, R, McKinlay, A F, Steinmetz, M, Vecchia, P, Whillock, M J. 1991. Proposals for basic restrictions for protection against occupational exposure to electromagnetic non-ionising radiations. Recommendations of an international Working Group set up under the auspices of the Commission of European Communities. *Physica Medica*, **VII**, 77–89.

Anderson, L E. 1991. Biological effects of extremely low-frequency electromagnetic fields: *in vivo* studies. *Radiat. Prot. Aust.* 9, 98–108.

Beischer, D E, and Knepton, J C, Jr. 1964. Influence of strong magnetic fields on the electrocardiogram of squirrel monkeys (*Samiri sciureus*). *Aerosp. Med.*, **35**, 939.

Beischer, D E, and Knepton, J C, Jr. 1966. The electroencephalogram of the squirrel monkey (*Saimiri sciureus*) in a very high magnetic field. Pensacola, Florida, NASA/Naval Aerospace Research Laboratory, NASA Order No. R-39.

Beniashvili, D Sh, Bilanishvili, V G, and Menabde, M Z. 1991. Low-frequency electromagnetic radiation enhances the induction of rat mammary tumours by nitrosomethy urea. *Cancer Lett.*, **61**, 75–79.

Berman, E, Chacon, L, House, D, Koch, B A, Koch, W E, Leal, J, Løvtrup, S, Mantiply, E, Martin, A H, Martucci, G I, Mild, K H, Monahan, J C, Sandström, M, Shamsaifer, K, Tell, R, Trillo, M A, Ubeda, A, and Wagner, P. 1990. Development of chicken embryos in a pulsed magnetic field. *Bioelectromagnetics*, **11**, 169–187.

Bernhardt, J H. 1988. The establishment of frequency dependent limits for electric and magnetic fields and evaluation of indirect effects. *Radiat. Environ. Biophys.*, **27**, 1-27.

Blank, M. 1992. Na,K-ATPase function in alternating electric fields. *FASEB J.*, **6**, 2434–2438.

Brent, R L, Gordon, W E, Bennett, W R, and Beckman, D A. 1993. Reproductive and teratologic effects of electromagnetic fields. *Reprod. Toxicol.*, **7**, 535–580.

Cain, C D, Thomas, D L, Moreno, L, and Adey, W R. 1992. 60 Hz magnetic fields and copromotion in carcinogenesis, *in vitro*. IN Abstracts, The First World Congress for Electricity and Magnetism in Biology and Medicine, Orlando, Florida, June 1992, p 30.

Chatterjee, I, Wu, D, and Gandhi, O P. 1986. Human body impedance and threshold currents for perception and pain for contact hazards analysis in the VLF-MF band. *IEEE Trans. Biomed. Eng.*, **BME-33**, p 486–494.

Chernoff, N, Rogers, J M, and Kavet, R. 1992. A review of the literature on potential reproductive and developmental toxicity of electric and magnetic fields. *Toxicology*, **74**, 91–126.

Clairmont, B A, Johnson, G B, Zaffanella, L E, and Zelingher, S. 1989. The effects of HVAC-HVDC line separation in a hybrid corridor. *IEEE Trans. Power Deliv.*, **4**, 1338–.

Cridland, N A. 1993. Electromagnetic fields and cancer: A review of relevant cellular studies. Chilton, NRPB-R256 (London, HMSO).

Dalziel, C F. 1954a. The threshold of perception currents. *IEEE Trans. Power App. Syst.*, **73**, PAS-90-996.

Dalziel, C F. 1954b. The threshold of perception currents. *Electr. Eng.*, **73**, 625–630.

D'Arsonval, A. 1896. Dispositifs pur la mesure des courants alternatifs de toutes frequences. *C.R. Soc. Biol. (Paris)*, **48**, 450.

de Lorge, J. 1979. Effects of magnetic fields on behaviour in nonhuman primates. In *Magnetic Field Effects on Biological Systems* (Tenforde, T S, ed). London, Plenum Press, p 37.

Deno, D W. 1974. Calculating electrostatic effects of overhead transmission lines. *IEEE Trans. Power Appl. Sys.*, **PAS-93**, 1458–1471.

Franceschetti, G, Gandhi, O P, and Grandolfo, M. (Eds) 1989. *Electromagnetic Biointeraction: Mechanisms, Safety Standards, Protection Guides*. New York and London, Plenum Press.

Goldberg, R B, and Creasey, W A. 1991. A review of cancer induction by extremely low frequency electromagnetic fields. Is there a plausible mechanism? *Med. Hypotheses*, **35**, 265–274.

Goodman, R, and Henderson, A M. 1991. Transcription and translation in cells exposed to extremely low frequency electromagnetic fields. *Bioelectrochem. Bioenerget.*, **25**, 333–355.

Grandolfo, M, Michaelson, S M, and Rindi, A. (Eds) 1983. *Biological Effects and Dosimetry of Non-ionising Radiation: Radiofrequency and Microwave Energies*. New York, Plenum Press.

Grandolfo, M, Michaelson, S M, and Rindi, A. (Eds) 1985. *Biological Effects and Dosimetry of Static and ELF Electromagnetic Fields*. New York, Plenum Press.

Greene, M H, Young, T I, and Clark, W H, Jr. 1981. Malignant melanoma in renal transplant recipients. *Lancet*, May 30, 1196–1199.

Guy, A W. 1985. Hazards of VLF electromagnetic fields. IN The impact of proposed radiofrequency radiation standards on military operations. Neuilly-sur-Seine, France, Advisory Group for Aerospace Research and Development (AGARD) (Lecture Series No. 138), pp 9.1–9.20.

Guy, A W, and Chou, C K. 1982. Hazard analysis: Very low frequency through medium frequency range. Brooks Air Force Base, USAF School of Aerospace Medicine, Aerospace Medical Division, Report USA FSAM 33615-78-d-0617.

Ham, W, Allen, R, Feeney Burns, L, Marmor, M, Power, L, Proctor, P, Sliney, D, and Wolbarsht, M. 1986. The involvement of retinal pigment epitelium (RPE). IN *Optical Radiation and Visual Health*. (Waxler, M, and Hitchins, V, eds). Boca Raton, CRC Press, pp 44–67.

Hauf, R. 1985. Haematological and biochemical effects of ELF fields in man - laboratory experiments. IN *Biological Effects and Dosimetry of Static and ELF Electromagnetic Fields* (Grandolfo, M, Michaelson, S M, and Rindi, A, eds). New York, Plenum Press, p 525.

Huuskonen, H, Juutilianen, J, and Komulainen, H. 1993. Effects of low frequency magnetic fields on fetal development in rats. *Bioelectromagnetics*, **14**, 205–213.

IARC. 1992. *Monographs on the evaluation of carcinogenic risk to humans. Solar and ultraviolet radiation*, **55**, Lyon, International Agency Research on Cancer.

IEC 1984. Effects of current passing through the body. International Electrochemical Commission IEC 471-1.

IEEE. 1978. Electric and magnetic field coupling from high voltage power transmission lines - classification of short-term effects of people. *IEEE Trans. Power App. Syst*, **PAS-79**, 2243–2252.

IRPA/INIRC 1988. International Radiation Protection Association/International Non Ionizing Radiation Committee. Guidelines on limits of exposure to radiofrequency electromagnetic fields in the frequency range from 100 kHz to 300 GHz. *Health Phys.* **54**, 115–123.

IRPA/INIRC 1989. Proposed changes to the IRPA/INIRC 1985 guidelines on limits of exposure to ultraviolet radiation. *Health Phys.*, **49**, 331–340.

IRPA/INIRC 1990. International Radiation Protection Association/International Non Ionizing Radiation Committee. Interim guidelines on limits of exposure to 50/60 Hz electric and magnetic fields. *Health Phys.* **58**, 113–122.

Kirschvink, J L, Kobayashi-Kirschvink, A, Diaz-Ricci, J C, and Kirschvink, S J. 1992. Magnetite in human tissues: A mechanism for the biological effects of weak ELF magnetic fields. *Bioelectromagnetics* (supplement) **1**, 101–113.

Kowalczuk, C I, Robbins, L, Thomas, J M, Butland, B K, and Saunders, R D. 1994. Effects of prenatal exposure to 50 Hz magnetic fields on development in mice. I: Implantation rate and fetal development. *Bioelectromagnetics*, **15**, 349–361.

Kowalczuk, C I, Sienkiewicz, Z J, and Saunders, R D. 1991. Biological effects of exposure to non-ionising electromagnetic fields and radiation. Chilton, NRPB-R238 (London, HMSO).

Kricker, A, Armstrong, B K, English, D R, and Heenan, P J. 1991. Pigmentary and cutaneous risk factors for non-melanocytic skin cancer - a case-control study. *Int. J. Cancer*, **48**, 650–662.

Kripke, M L. 1974. Antigenicity of murine skin tumors induced by ultraviolet light. *J. Natl. Cancer Inst.*, **53**, 1333–1336.

Kühne, B. 1980. Einfluss elektrischer 50-Hz-Felder hoher Feldstärke auf den menschlichen Organismus. Köln, Institut zur Erforschung elektrischer Unfälle, Medizinisch-Technischer Bericht (in German).

Larkin, W D, and Reilly, J P. 1984. Strength duration relationship for electrocutaneous sensitivity: Stimulation by capacitive discharges. *Percept. Psychophys.*, **36**, 68–78.

Leung, F C, Rommereim, D N, Stevens, R G, Wilson, B W, Buschbom, R L, and Anderson, L E. 1988. Effects of electric fields on rat mammary tumour development induced by 7, 12-dimethylbenz(a)anthracene. IN Abstracts, 10th Annual Meeting of the Bioelectromagnetics Society, June 1988, Stamford, Connecticut, p 2.

Liboff, A R. 1987. Geomagnetic cyclotron resonance in living cells. *J. Biol. Phys.*, **13**, 99–102.

Liburdy, R P. 1992. Calcium signalling in lymphocytes and ELF fields. Evidence for an electric field metric and a site of interaction involving the calcium ion channel. *FEBS Lett.*, **301**, 53–59.

Lorimore, S A, Kowalczuk, C I, Saunders, R D, and Wright, E G. 1990. Lack of acute effects of 20 mT, 50 Hz magnetic fields on murine haemopoiesis. *Int. J. Radiat. Biol.*, **58**, 713–723.

Löscher, W, Mevissen, M, Lehmacher, W, and Stamm, A. 1993. Tumour promotion in a breast cancer model by exposure to a weak alternating magnetic field. *Cancer Lett.*, **71**, 75–81.

Lyle, D B, Doshi, J, Fuchs, T A, Casamento, J P, Sei, Y, Arora, P K, and Swicord, M L. 1992. Intracellular calcium signalling by JURKAT E6-1cells exposed to an induced 1 mV/cm 60 Hz, sinusoidal electric field. IN *Electricity and Magnetism in Biology and Medicine. Proceedings of the First World Congress for Electricity and Magnetism in Biology and Medicine, Orlando, Florida, 1992* (Blank, M, ed). San Francisco, San Francisco Press, 307–310.

Magnus, K. 1991. The nordic profile of skin cancer incidence. A comparative epidemiological study of the three main types of skin cancer. *Int. J. Cancer*, **47**, 12–19.

Marshall, J. 1987. Ultraviolet radiation and the eye. IN *Human Exposure to Ultraviolet-Radiation: Risk and Regulations*, (Passchier, W, and Bosnjacovic, B, eds). Amsterdam, pp 125–142.

Massof, R, Sykes, S, Rapp, L, Robinson, W, Zwick, H, and Hocheimer, B. 1986. Optical radiation damage to ocular photoreceptors: IN *Optical Radiation and Visual Health* (Waxler, M, and Hitchins, V eds). Boca Raton, CRC Press, pp. 69–87.

McCann, J, Dietrich, F, Rafferty, C, and Martin, A O. 1993. A critical review of the genotoxic potential of electric and magnetic fields. *Mutat. Res.*, **297**, 61–95.

McKinlay, A F, and Diffey, B L. 1987. A reference action spectrum for ultra-violet induced erythema in human skin. *CIE J.*, **6**, 17–22.

McLauchlan, K A. 1992. Are environmental magnetic fields dangerous? *Phys. World*, January, 41–45.

McLean, J R N, Stuchly, M A, Mitchel, R E J, Wilkinson, D, Yang, H, Goddard, M, Lecuyer, D W, Schunk, M, Callary, E, and Morrison, D. 1991. Cancer promotion in a mouse-skin model by a 60-Hz magnetic field: II. Tumour development and immune response. *Bioelectromagnetics*, **12**, 273–287.

McRobbie, D, and Foster, M A. 1984. Thresholds for biological effects of time-varying magnetic fields. *Clin. Phys. Physiol. Meas.*, **5** No. 2, 67–78.

Mevissen, M, Stamm, A, Buntenkötter, S, Zwingelberg, R, Wahnschaffe, U, and Löscher, W. 1993. Effects of magnetic fields on mammary tumour development induced by 7,12-dimethylbenz(a)anthracene in rats. *Bioelectromagnetics*, **14**, 131–143.

Murphy, J C, Kaden, D A, Warren, J and Sivak, A. 1993. Power frequency electric and magnetic fields: a review of genetic toxicology. *Mutat. Res.*, **296**, 221–240.

NRPB. 1992. Electromagnetic fields and the risk of cancer. *Doc. NRPB*, **3** No. 1, 1–138.

NRPB. 1993. Board statement on restrictions on human exposure to static and time varying electromagnetic fields and radiation. *Doc. NRPB*, **4**, No. 5, 1–63.

NRPB. 1994. Health effects relating to the use of visual display units. *Doc. NRPB*, **5** No. 2, 1–75.

ORAU, 1992. Health effects of low frequency electric and magnetic fields. A report prepared by an Oak Ridge Associated Universities Panel for The Committee on Interagency Radiation Research and Policy Coordination. Oak Ridge, ORAU 92/F8.

Ortel, B, and Gange, R W. 1992. UV-A acting spectra for erythema and pigmentation. IN *Biological Responses to Ultraviolet Radiation* (Urbach, F, ed). Overland Park, Valdenmar Publishing Co.

Parrish, J A, Jaenicke, K F, and Anderson, R R. 1982. Erythema and melanogenesis action spectra of normal human skin. *Photochem. Photobiol.*, **36**, 187–191.

Pathak, M A, and Fanselow, D L. 1983. Photobiology of melanin pigmentation; dose/response of skin to sunlight and its contents. *J. Am. Acad. Dermatol.*, **9**, 724–733.

Pitts, G, Cameron, L, Jose, L, Lerman, S, Moss, E, Varma, S, Zigler, S, Zigman, S, and Zuclich, J, 1986. Optical radiation and cataracts. IN *Optical Radiation and Visual Health* (Waxler, M and Hitchins, V, eds). Boc Raton, CRC Press, pp 5–41.

Rannug, A, Ekström, T, Hansson Mild, K, Holmberg, B, Gimenez-Conti, I, and Slaga, T, 1993. A study on skin tumour formation in mice with 50 Hz magnetic field exposure. *Carcinogenesis*, **14**, No. 4, 537–578.

Reilly, J P. 1978. Electric and magnetic field coupling form high voltage AC power transmission lines-classification of short-term effects on people. *IEEE Trans. Power App. Sys.*, **PAS-97**, 2243–2252.

Reiter, R J. 1992. Changes in the circadian melatonin synthesis in the pineal gland of animals exposed to extremely low frequency electromagnetic radiation: A summary of observations and speculation on their implications. IN (Moore-Ede, M C, Campbell, S S, and Reiter, R J, eds). IN *Electromagnetic Fields and Circadian Rhythmicity* Boston, Birkhäuser, pp 13–27.

Rogers, S J. 1977. RF shock/burn hazards in the MF/HF band. Portsmouth, Admiralty Surface Weapons Establishment. WP/XSA/7503.

Rommereim, D N, Rommereim, R L, Sikov, M R, Buschbom, R L, and Anderson, L E, 1990. Reproduction, growth and development of rats during chronic exposure to multiple field strengths of 60-Hz electric fields. *Fundam. Appl. Toxicol.*, 14, 608–621.

Salzinger, K, Freimark S, McCollough, M, Phillips, D, Birenbaum, L. 1990. Altered operant behaviour of adult rats after perinatal exposure to a 60-Hz electromagnetic field. *Bioelectromagnetics* 11, 105–116.

Saunders, R D, Kowalczuk, C I, and Sienkiewicz, Z J. 1991. Biological effects of exposure to non-ionising electromagnetic radiation. III. Radiofrequency and microwave radiation. Chilton, NRPB-R240 (London, HMSO).

Schenck, J F, Dunmoulin, C L, Redington, R W, Kressel, H Y, Elliott, R T, and McDougall, I L. 1992. Human exposure to 4-tesla magnetic fields in a whole-body scanner. *Med. Phys.*, 19, 1089–1098.

Sienkiewicz, Z J, Cridland, N A, Kowalczuk, C I, and Saunders, R D, 1993. Biological effects of electromagnetic fields and radiation. IN *Review of Radio Science* (Ross Stone, W, ed). Oxford, Oxford University Press, pp 737–770.

Sienkiewicz, Z J, Kowalczuk, C I, and Saunders, R D. 1991. Biological effects of exposure to non-ionising electromagnetic fields and radiation: II. Extremely low frequency electric and magnetic fields. Chilton, NRPB-R239 (London, HMSO).

Sienkiewicz, Z J, Robbins, L, Haylock, R G E, and Saunders, R D, 1994. Effects of prenatal exposure to 50 Hz magnetic fields on development in mice. II Postnatal development and behaviour. *Bioelectromagnetics*, 15, 363–375.

Sikov, M R, Rommereim, D N, Beamer, J L, Buschbom, R L, Kaune, W T, and Phillips, R D. 1987. Developmental studies of Hanford miniature swine exposed to 60-Hz electric fields. *Bioelectromagnetics*, 8, 229–242.

Stevens, R G, Davis S, Thomas, D B, Anderson, L E, and Wilson, B W, 1992. Electric power, pineal function, and the risk of breast cancer. *FASEB J.*, 6, 853–860.

Stuchly, M A, McLean, J R N, Burnett, R, Goddard, M, Lecuyer, D W, and Mitchel, R E J. 1992. Modification of tumour promotion in the mouse skin by exposure to an alternating magnetic field. *Cancer Lett.*, 65, 1–7.

Tenforde, T S, and Kaune, W. 1987. Interaction of extremely low frequency electric and magnetic fields with humans. *Health Phys.*, 53, pp 595-606.

Tsong, T Y, 1992. Molecular recognition and processing of periodic signals in cells: Study of activation of membrane ATPases by alternating electric fields. *Biochem. Biophys. Acta*, 1113, 53–70.

Tucker, R D, and Schmitt, O H. 1978. Tests for human perception of 60 Hz moderate magnetic fields. *IEEE Trans. Biomed. Eng.*, **BME-25**, 509.

UNEP/WHO/IRPA, 1984. *Extremely low frequency (ELF) fields. Environmental Health Criteria 35.* Geneva, World Health Organisation.

UNEP/WHO/IRPA, 1987. *Magnetic Fields. Environmental Health Criteria 69*, Geneva, World Health Organization.

UNEP/WHO/IRPS 1989. *Electromagnetic fields (300 Hz to 300 GHz). Environmental Health Criteria 137*, Geneva: WHO.

US Department of Health and Human Services, 1990. Medications that increase sensitivity to light: A 1990 listing HHS Publications FDA 90-8280.

Walleczek, J, and Liburdy, R P, 1990. Nonthermal 60 Hz sinusoidal magnetic-field exposure enhances $^{45}Ca^{2+}$ uptake in rat thymocytes: Dependence on mitogen activation. *FEBS Lett.*, 271, 157–160.

Walleczek, J, Miller, P L, and Adey, W R, 1992. Simultaneous dual-sample fluorimetric detection of real-time effects of ELF electromagnetic fields on cytosolic free calcium and divalent cation flux in human leukaemic T-cells (JURKAT). In: *Electricity and Magnetism in Biology and Medicine. Proceedings of the First World Congress for Electricity and Magnetism in Biology and Medicine, Orlando, Florida.* Blank, M ed., 303–306, San Francisco, San Francisco Press.

Wever, R. 1970. The effects of electric fields on circadian rhythmicity in men. *Life Sci. Space Res.*, 8, 177.

Wiley, M J, Corey, P, Kavet, R, Charry, J, Harvey, S, Agnew, D, Walsh, M. 1992. The effects of continuous exposure to 20 kHz sawtooth magnetic fields on the litters of CD1 mice. *Teratology*, 46, 391–398.

Wilson, B W, and Anderson, L E, 1990. ELF electromagnetic-field induced effects on the pineal gland. IN *Extremely Low Frequency Electromagnetic Fields: The Question of Cancer.* (Wilson, B W, Stevens, R G, and Anderson, L E, eds). Columbus, Ohio, Battelle Press, 159–186.

Wilson, B W, Stevens, R G, and Anderson, L E, 1989. Mini review: Neuroendocrine mediated effects of electromagnetic-field exposure: Possible role of the pineal gland. *Life Sci.*, 45, 1319–1332.

Wilson, B W, Wright, C W, Morris, J E, Buschbom, R L, Brown D P, Miller, D L, Sommers-Flannigan, R, and Anderson, L E. 1990. Evidence for an effect of ELF electromagnetic fields on human pineal gland function. *J. Pineal Res.*, 9, 259–269.

Yasui, M, Kikuchi, T, Otaka, Y, and Kato, M, 1989. Life span exposure of rats to 50 Hz sinusoidal alternating magnetic fields. In: *Electricity and Magnetism in Biology and Medicine. Proceedings of the First World Congress for Electricity and Magnetism in Biology and Medicine, Orlando, Florida.* Blank, M ed., 839–841, San Francisco, San Francisco Press.

5   Human health studies

5.1   Static fields

Only a few epidemiological studies of groups with occupational exposures to static magnetic fields have been performed. As with the studies of time varying fields, measurements of field levels are generally not available. An exception is a study of workers at a chloralkali plant exposed to fields up to 30 mT for whom no increased cancer risk was found, although the number of workers was small.

5.2   Time varying electromagnetic fields of frequencies less then 100 kHz

Epidemiological studies are particularly difficult to carry out in the case of time varying electromagnetic field exposure because such fields are universally present in the modern environment. To date over 40 studies have examined the health effects of power frequency fields. This work has been comprehensively reviewed by Coleman and Beral (1988), the Electric Power Research Institute (EPRI 1989), the Italian National Institute of Health (Grandolfo *et al* 1989), the National Radiological Protection Board (NRPB 1992, 1993, 1994a), Oak Ridge Associated Universities (ORAU 1992), Cartwright (1993), Savitz (1993) and the National Board of Health of the Danish Ministry of Health (DMH 1994).

Three categories of exposure have been considered in these studies. These are: fields in the ordinary residential environment, fields produced by electrical appliances, and fields in the workplace, especially where people work close to electrical equipment. For historic reasons, the health endpoint that has been most studied as a potential risk from exposure to fields is cancer.

5.2.1   Cancer

The main cancers studied have been childhood cancer, brain cancer, leukaemia and breast cancer:

- Childhood cancer, particularly leukaemia (Wertheimer and Leeper 1979, Fulton *et al* 1980, McDowell 1986, Tomenius 1986, Savitz *et al* 1988, Severson *et al* 1988, Savitz and Feingold 1989, Coleman *et al* 1989, Lin and Lu 1989, Myers *et al* 1990, London *et al* 1991, Feychting and Ahlbom 1993, Olsen *et al* 1993, Verkalaso *et al* 1993).

- Brain cancer (for example, Floderus *et al* 1993).

- Breast cancer (for example, Matanoski *et al* 1991, Stevens 1987, Tynes and Anderson 1990, Tynes *et al* 1992).

Some studies reporting a cancer increase in children and adults postulate a connection with exposure to very weak (0.1 to 1.0 µT) 50 or 60 Hz magnetic fields. Magnetic fields of this magnitude occur in the normal environment. Theoretical knowledge about effective mechanisms of magnetic fields (UNEP/WHO/IRPA 1987) is not able to support this. The body currents induced by such magnetic fields are more than two orders of magnitude lower than the naturally occurring currents in the body. In epidemiological studies, magnetic flux density is the main measure used. However, it is uncertain whether spot measurement (at certain times), time-weighted average exposures or peak events are more relevant. From the conventional toxicological standpoint time-weighted average exposures appear more soundly based.

The results of epidemiological studies are expressed as relative risk ratios for different cancers in the populations studied. The relative risk ratio is a measure of the factor by which the risk is raised in the population studied compared with a control population. While uncertainties in the results are great because it is difficult to determine exposure, and because of some inherent uncertainties in these types of study, statistical correlations between electrical exposure and certain cancers appear to be more consistent than others across the studies published.

Certain features have emerged from the studies published:

- The risk ratio is predominantly in the range between 1.2 and 3 for leukaemia. It is found that the ratio taken for all leukaemias is only slightly above 1 and when acute myeloid leukaemias are examined alone, the risk ratio is higher, consistently above 3. Childhood leukaemia appears to have a possible association with field exposure.

- Most risk ratios for brain cancer and work exposure are between 1 and 2.

- Male breast cancer risks appear high for electrical workers, and is of particular interest because of the possibility that the putative pineal effect might be a pathway to causing this type of cancer.

The most important epidemiological studies have been reviewed and evaluated by several national and international radiation protection bodies.

In its 1992 report, the NRPB Advisory Group (NRPB 1992) considered seven studies published in peer-reviewed journals (Wertheimer and Leeper 1979, Fulton *et al* 1980, Tomenius 1986, Savitz *et al* 1988, Coleman *et al* 1989, Myers *et al* 1990, London *et al* 1991) up to 1991, all of the case-control type in which comparisons were made between the proximity of various sources of electromagnetic fields to the places of residence of children who had or who had not developed cancer. The results were variable, but taken at face value, appeared to provide some evidence of an association. This evidence was less weak for brain cancer than for leukaemia and less weak when, in the case of studies in the USA, exposure was estimated from local `wiring configurations' rather than from proximity to sources of electromagnetic fields or from measurements in the home. However, wiring configurations are associated with other characteristics of a house, other than EM field exposure, and the associations between wiring configurations and cancer may be due to confounding. This possibility is given credence by the fact that these studies (Savitz *et al* 1988 and London *et al* 1991) that contributed most weight to the significant findings selected controls by methods that may well be biased with respect to socioeconomic status and stability of residence. The major positive results from these studies may in consequence be artefacts of the method of enquiry.

Since 1991, results have been published for national studies of childhood cancer and residential EM field exposure in Sweden (Feychting and Ahlbom 1993), Denmark (Olsen *et al* 1993) and Finland (Verkasalo *et al* 1993). These studies were similar in design, in that they each utilised national population and cancer registers. In addition, assessments of historical exposures to EM fields from power lines were made, using records held by electrical utilities. The NRPB Advisory Group considered that these studies were well controlled and substantially better than those that previous reported associations with childhood cancer.

TABLE 5.1 Childhood cancer and 50 Hz magnetic fields in three Nordic studies (Ahlbom et al 1993)

Study	Leukaemia No[b]	Leukaemia RR[c] (95% CI)	Nervous system tumour No[b]	Nervous system tumour RR[c] (95% CI)	Lymphoma No[b]	Lymphoma RR[c] (95% CI)	Total[a] No[b]	Total[a] RR[c] (95% CI)
Sweden7		2.7 (1.0-6.3)	2	0.7 (0.1-2.7)	2	1.3 (0.2-5.1)	12	1.1 (0.5-2.1)
Denmark		1.5 (0.3-6.7)	2	1.0 (0.2-5.0)	1	5.0 (0.3-82)	6[b]	1.5 (0.6-4.1)
Finland3		1.6 (0.3-4.5)	5[d]	2.3 (0.8-5.4)	0	0.0 (0.0-4.2)	11	1.5 (0.7-2.7)
Total 13		2.1 (1.1-4.1)	9	1.5 (0.7-3.2)	3	1.0 (0.3-3.7)	29	1.3 (0.9-2.1)

Notes

a   All childhood cancers (Sweden and Finland) or all leukaemias, nervous system tumours and lymphomas (Denmark).

b   Number of cancers at fields above 0.2 µT (Sweden and Finland) or 0.25 µT (Denmark).

c   Relative risk.

d   Including three tumours in one boy. An analysis based on the number of affected children gives RR = 1.4 (95% CI 0.0-3.7).

Table 5.1 presents the results of a meta-analysis conducted by the authors of the three Nordic studies (Ahlbom et al 1993). The only cancer type showing a statistically significant association with calculated historical magnetic fields is leukaemia, although based on a total of only 13 cases in the upper exposure category. The study contributing most to this finding is that in Sweden, although this study showed no association with childhood leukaemia when based on measurements of magnetic fields in homes rather than on calculated historical values (Feychting and Ahlbom 1993). No statistically significant findings arose for other cancers, table 5.1. Although the Finnish study (Verkasalo et al 1993) reported a raised risk for nervous system tumours, this result was influenced heavily by one boy with neurofibromatosis who developed three tumours. An analysis of these data based on the number of affected individuals rather than the number of tumours provides no evidence of an excess.

In contrast to suggestions from earlier, poorly-controlled studies, the recent Nordic studies do not therefore indicate that any increased risk would be of brain cancer. The NRPB Advisory Group concluded that these studies do not establish that exposure to electromagnetic fields is a cause of cancer, but that, taken together, they do provide some evidence to suggest the possibility exists in the case of childhood leukaemia. The number of affected children in the studies is, however, very small (NRPB 1994a).

Few data are available on the risk of cancer in adults in relation to residential EM field exposure. Those studies that have been conducted, such as the national study in Sweden (Feychting and Ahlbom 1993), have not suggested the existence of any hazard.

The greatest amount of epidemiological data concerning EM fields relates to exposure at work. However, most of the studies conducted have attempted to characterise EM field exposures on the basis of job title rather than field measurements. In a review of such studies, the NRPB Advisory Group concluded that a tendency for the selective publication of results that suggest an increased risk might explain the very small overall excess of leukaemia implied by the totality of these data. It is notable that welders, who receive the highest exposures to extremely low frequency EM fields do not have a raised leukaemia risk. Publication bias seemed to be less likely to explain the somewhat greater, but still small, excess of brain cancer in these studies, although the possibility that some chemical may be responsible could not be excluded.

Since 1992, the results of some occupational studies that incorporate EM field measurements have been published. A study in Sweden (Floderus *et al* 1993) claimed to show an association with chronic lymphatic leukaemia, although low participation rates and the high level of surrogate measurements raise the possibility of bias. There were also methodological problems with a study of US telephone linemen (Matanoski *et al* 1993), related to case ascertainment and to the relevance of current measurements in estimating past exposures. A study of 36,000 electrical utility workers in the USA did not show associations between EM fields and leukaemia, lymphoma or brain cancer (Sahl *et al* 1993); similar findings arose from a smaller study of railway workers in Norway (Tynes *et al* 1994).

TABLE 5.2 Relative risk of cancer in relation to cumulative exposure to magnetic fields among French and Canadian electrical utility workers (Thériault *et al* 1994)

Cancer	Exposure group	
	≥ Median[a]	≥ 90th percentile[b]
Leukaemia (140)[c]	1.54 (0.90 - 2.63)[d]	1.75 (0.77 - 3.96)
Chronic lymphatic leukaemia (41)	1.48 (0.50 - 4.40)	1.71 (0.44 - 6.66)
Acute non-lymphatic leukaemia (60)	2.41 (1.07 - 5.44)	2.52 (0.70 - 9.09)
Malignant brain cancer (108)	1.54 (0.85 - 2.81)	1.95 (0.76 - 5.00)
All cancers (4,151)	1.01 (0.91 - 1.13)	1.01 (0.86 - 1.20)

Notes
a Median exposure = 3.1 μT - years.
b 90th percentile of exposure = 15.7 μT - years.
c Number of cases.
d 95% confidence interval.

The largest occupational study involving EM field measurements was based on 170,000 electrical utility workers in France and over 50,000 such workers in Canada (Ontario and Quebec) (Thériault *et al* 1994). Table 2 summaries the results in relation to estimated cumulative exposure. There was no evidence for an association with total cancer incidence. There was a statistically significant raised risk for acute non-lymphatic leukaemia (ANLL) but not for other leukaemia sub-types. However, there was heterogeneity between the cohorts in that the ANLL finding was apparent only in Ontario, and there did not appear to be a trend of increasing risk with increasing exposure. No statistically significant findings arose for brain cancer or for any of the other 29 types of cancer studied.

The studies published since the original NRPB Advisory Group report have therefore strengthened the evidence for believing that some groups of workers in industries where exposure to electromagnetic fields may have been particularly elevated have had an increased risk of leukaemia, but not of brain cancer (NRPB 1994a). The results of the new studies are, however, neither consistent in the type of leukaemia found to be increased nor consistent in finding a progressive increase with progressive exposure.

Several case-control studies have been conducted on the occupations of fathers of children with central nervous system tumours or neuroblastomas, in relation to the father's potential for occupational exposure to EM fields at the time of the child's birth. The NRPB Advisory Group concluded that, with the weak evidence available and the low quality of the exposure data in these studies, no conclusion was possible. Two studies have reported on childhood cancer in relation to the use of electrical appliances (Myers *et al* 1990, Savitz *et al* 1990). While these studies suggested some associations with the use of electrical over-blankets, the possibility of recall bias and uncertainty about the representative nature of the controls led the NRPB Advisory Group to conclude that the results are incapable of interpretation. Studies of adult cancer have not shown any relationship with electrical appliance use.

Recently, the International Commission on Non-Ionizing Radiation Protection (ICNIRP) reviewed the data about possible carcinogenicity of power frequency magnetic fields. This review considered all scientific data that have been published or publicly presented since 1992. The Commission concluded that most recent data reflect some improvements in methodology in laboratory studies and in epidemiological studies of both occupational and general populations. After careful considerations of this evidence, ICNIRP concluded that the data related to cancer do not provide a basis for health risk assessment on human exposure to power frequency fields. Accordingly they confirmed the interim guidelines published in 1990 (IRPA/INIRC 1990). They undertook to periodically review new evidence in this area as it develops.

5.2.2   General effects on health

Epidemiological studies on exposure to electromagnetic fields and general effects on health have been reviewed by Dennis et al (1992).

Early reports from the former USSR of adverse effects on health associated with exposures to electromagnetic fields at both low and microwave frequencies as well as static magnetic fields led to determined efforts in other countries to confirm these findings (Dennis *et al* 1992). Long-term exposures to power frequencies, microwaves or magnetic fields were alleged in the Russian reports to produce very similar non-specific symptoms, ie, tiredness, headaches, nausea, loss of sexual potency, cardiovascular effects, sleep disturbances, anxiety and changes in blood cell concentrations and blood chemistry. Cardiovascular changes and central nervous system effects were particularly emphasised. Data in these reports were often sparse, the reports impressionistic, without proper control populations and the selection of the study population itself essentially *post hoc*, ie, based on a prior history of complaint by the workers concerned.

Attempts to verify the Russian observations have included surveys of exposed groups and carefully controlled laboratory experiments with volunteers. Although some reports have tended to support the early Russian work, other and particularly more recent studies do not give such support Strumza (1970), for instance, provides an account of a health events survey made of male employees of the French power company Electricité de France. In total 144 such men, all living in rural areas, were included, together with their wives (129) and children (252). Medical and social security records covering almost 1900 man years in all were scanned, thus assuring an objective recording of health events. Employees and, in turn, wives and children were classified as ` exposed' if place of residence and workplace were closer than 25 m to high voltage (220–400 kV) cables, and ` not exposed' if they lived and worked more than 125 m removed from such cables. All men of intermediate exposure status were excluded from the study at an earlier stage. For four separate measures of expressed demand for medical services and drugs, the results showed quite clearly no tendency for the exposed group to   consume' more than the non-exposed group. This observation held for men, women and children. The analysis appears to have controlled for variation in neighbourhood type.

A report by Broadbent *et al* (1985) was an attempt to measure non-specific health effects in electric power transmission and distribution workers. This was achieved by using a schedule of derived health status indices obtained from both reported health events and a variant of the Middlesex Hospital Questionnaire (MHQ). This is a standardised instrument with the main advantages that it can be administered by non-medical staff and that a range of expected values is available for the various subsections of the questionnaire (Depression, Somatic Symptoms, Obsessional Symptoms, etc) based on past examples of its use. A small number of questions in addition to those of MHQ were asked, for instance, about visits to the general practitioner, intake of medicines and experience of headaches. All the health indices are thus based on subjective self-assessment. Unlike most other studies, objective measurements of exposure were made with personal dosemeters, although only of electric field exposure. These dosemeters were worn for periods of 2 weeks, providing data on 287 subjects. In addition, prior estimates of exposure were available as informed, but ultimately subjective, engineering judgements. These exposures were expressed in terms of the product of the electric field strength and the time spent in the field, ie, in kilovolt hours per metre (kV h m^{-1}). It emerged at the end of the study period that the measured exposures were generally much lower than those estimated. This finding has implications for other studies in which exposures are based on subjective and surrogate indices of exposure.

The study was sufficiently sensitive to show clear differences in health between job categories and geographical districts in which the work took place. Adverse health effects correlated with lack of job satisfaction, personal domestic problems, working alone, working long hours, and recent changes in shift times. There were no adverse health effects associated with higher exposure levels. The implied annual occupational exposures averaged about 150 kV h m^{-1}, but ranged up to 500 kV h m^{-1}. These may be compared with the average domestic exposure of the general population in the USA of 70 kV h m^{-1} (Silva *et al* 1985). It is not possible to say what they represent in terms of magnetic field exposures, but the members of the study population will undoubtedly have been exposed to higher fields than experienced by the general population, possibly by factors of between 10 and 100.

This absence of any adverse health effects related to power frequency electromagnetic field exposure broadly confirms the findings of other health surveys of occupationally exposed persons undertaken in the last decade in Europe and North America (Singewald *et al* 1973, Malboysson 1976, Roberge 1976, Stopps and Janischewsky 1979, Knave *et al* 1979, Baroncelli *et al* 1986, Gamberale *et al* 1989). Each of these surveys examined railway or power workers' health and found no significant excess of adverse effects in subgroups with higher electromagnetic field exposures by comparison with controls or unexposed populations.

5.3   Electromagnetic fields and radiation of frequencies between 100 kHz and 300 GHz

Epidemiological studies related to putative exposure to electromagnetic fields and radiation of frequencies between 100 kHz and 300 GHz have been extensively reported in several reviews (for example, Dennis *et al* 1992, NRPB 1992, UNEP/WHO/IRPA 1993).

5.3.1 Pregnancy outcome and reproduction

A few studies investigated possible effects on the offspring of paternal exposure to radiofrequency radiation. Also in this case, the results were contradictory, possibly due to deficiencies in retrospective assessment of exposure.

A much larger number of studies have been carried out on pregnancy outcome of exposed women. Epidemiological studies have been performed on operators of RF welding machines and on physiotherapists (Larsen et al 1991, Ouellet-Hellstrom and Stewart 1993). Once again, the results were somewhat conflicting, and only suggestive of the need for further study.

However, concern about the effects of electromagnetic fields on pregnancy has mainly been expressed with regard to the use of visual display units (VDUs). After some epidemiological data suggested a possible increase in spontaneous abortion among operators of VDUs, a large number of similar studies were conducted to test the validity of this hypothesis.

The majority of these investigations, including the most recent and accurate in defining the exposure conditions, have failed to replicate the findings of first investigators. In particular, extensive and well controlled case-control studies recently performed in Canada, the USA and the UK, indicated no association between exposure and miscarriage that seems to indicate that the previous studies were poorly designed and their results were erroneous (Marcus 1990).

The NRPB Advisory Group on Non-ionising Radiation has examined the experimental and epidemiological evidence related to the adverse pregnancy outcome and use of VDUs. The Group concluded that overall the results indicated that VDU use does not increase the risk of spontaneous abortion and that the risk of congenital malformations does not appear to be increased in women who have used VDUs in early pregnancy (NRPB 1994b).

5.3.2 Cancer

In the last few years, several epidemiological studies have suggested an association between long-term exposure to magnetic fields and the development of cancers, mainly leukaemia and brain tumours. Most of these studies investigated extremely low frequency fields, while only few investigations have been carried out on radiofrequency radiation. Finally, several studies, mainly of a retrospective nature, have addressed exposures to electromagnetic fields of unspecified or mixed frequency.

In contrast with ELF, where many residential studies have been performed, very few epidemiological data exist on exposure of the general public to RF. A study of cancer incidence in areas with or without broadcasting towers in Hawaii was suggestive of a possible relationship with electromagnetic fields, because of the very limited number of cases and of the lack of information on exposure.

The data collected on the personnel of the American Embassy in Moscow (Lillienfeld et al 1978), who had been irradiated with microwaves for many years, provides some insight into possible health effects of long-term exposure to low level fields. No convincing evidence of any health risk was provided by the study.

Studies on occupational exposures are important to verify the plausibility of carcinogenic effects of electromagnetic fields, even though the exposure levels and conditions are very different from those experienced by the general public. Once again, the results of different studies are not very consistent. A study on military radar operators only suggested a slight tendency toward an increased risk of cancer in general (Robinette et al 1980). On the other hand, a retrospective mortality survey of amateur radio operators showed an increase of leukaemia, particularly acute myeloid, but also a statistically significant decrease of several other cancers (Milham 1988).

Recently, a mortality investigation on workers in an electromagnetic pulse (EMP) test programme suggested an association between death due to leukaemia and employment in this area (Muhm 1992). The study, however, suffers from severe limitations because of the limited number of cases, and the peculiarity of the job, involving a number of confounders.

Many occupational studies on electromagnetic fields and cancer were based on job classification as an indirect evaluation of exposure. These studies were aimed at detecting possible associations of cancer with ELF field exposure (NRPB 1992, ORAU 1992). Workers in the electrical and electronics industry are often considered as a category with potential electromagnetic field exposure. In this case, the relative role of low and high frequency fields is obviously difficult to separate and data can therefore be considered only suggestive of possible associations of cancer with either fields. Such workers may also be exposed to chemical agents.

Prevailing exposure to RF radiation alone is likely to occur in the telecommunications industry, where some investigations reported an increased incidence of malignant melanoma.

The epidemiological literature on electromagnetic fields and cancer has been critically reviewed by individual authors, and by several national commissions and international organizations. Most of them dealt only with ELF fields, but the NRPB Advisory Group examined available data for both ELF and RF/MW fields (NRPB 1992). The conclusion is that there is no clear evidence of a carcinogenic hazard from the normal levels of power frequency electromagnetic fields, radiofrequency or microwave radiation to which people are exposed. Similar conclusion were drawn by all the above mentioned commissions for ELF fields.

5.3.3   Cataracts

A great number of papers have been published reporting various syndromes in workers presumably exposed to electromagnetic fields higher than ` normal' environmental levels.

Ocular effects have been widely investigated because the eye is considered as a critical organ due to its poor vascularisation. General eye irritation has sometimes been described in studies on workers exposed to RF fields.

The induction of opacities and cataracts has been investigated in several case-control studies on workers exposed to high intensity microwave radiation, with contradictory results. Some of the studies show a statistically significant increase of ocular damage in workers exposed to high fields; however, quantitative evaluations of exposure have rarely been performed. The damage seems to be related to accelerated aging of the lens tissue in exposed workers with respect to the general public. In one study, a correlation has also been established between the increase of lens modifications and the duration and intensity of exposure. A number of other epidemiological surveys show no difference in ocular pathologies between exposed workers and controls.

In conclusion, although a possible association between lens damages and exposure to high intensity microwave fields has been suggested, there is no clear evidence that radiofrequency and microwave fields can give rise to any effect on the eye at the low levels that are usually experienced by the general public.

5.3.4   General effects on health

Many findings have been reported on the general health status of workers exposed to RF/MW radiation, mainly in industry or among military personnel. A wide variety of conditions, symptoms, diseases, and clinical measurements have been described. Early clinical reports from the former USSR and other Eastern European countries claimed a collection of symptoms, such as headache, sleeplessness, weakness, lessened libido, etc, which were variously defined as neurasthenic syndrome, or chronic overexposure syndrome, or microwave syndrome. These findings, however, have not been replicated in later studies. Given the subjective nature of the complaints, it is likely that other factors may be responsible for the disturbances, in particular a reporting bias due to the awareness of the exposure and of the possible microwave sickness syndrome. This hypothesis seems to be confirmed by recent results of studies on hypersensitivity, where individuals who felt special sensations in the presence of very low fields failed in general to distinguish true from sham exposure to RF radiation (Hamnerius *et al* 1993). The role of confounding factors, in particular of other noxious agents in the workplace, is also relevant in the evaluation of medical findings. Careful investigations on radar workers complaining of microwave syndrome have shown no significant alteration in objective parameters such as biochemical and haematological data, ECG, nervous and cardiovascular activity. An analysis of the working environment suggested that the symptoms could probably be due to noise, or to the air quality (bad ventilation).

In conclusion, comparative clinical studies do not provide any clear evidence of adverse health effects of exposure to RF in the workplace, under normal working conditions. A few reports on accidental overexposures to RF fields give useful information on possible threshold levels for some health effect. In particular, exposures to power densities up to 100 W m^{-2} were not found to result in any harmful effect. Warmth sensation, which lasted during exposure, was detected by half of workers accidentally exposed to RF power density of about 100 W m^{-2}, while effects on the nervous system, with symptoms as anxiety and hypertension, lasted several months after exposure to power densities one order of magnitude higher (Graham 1985).

5.4   Optical radiation

This section summarises epidemiological evidence on exposure to optical radiation and the risks of adverse health effects. The greatest number and variety of epidemiological studies in this area relate to exposure to ultraviolet radiation. There are relatively few studies related to exposure to visible or infrared radiation.

5.4.1   Ultraviolet radiation

The principal risk and public health concern related to exposure to ultraviolet radiation is skin cancer and the majority of ultraviolet radiation epidemiological studies have addressed this subject. However, studies have also been carried out on the risk of cancer of the lip, ocular malignant melanoma and cataract. A number of comprehensive reviews of epidemiological studies related to UVR exposure and adverse effects on human health , particularly skin cancer, have been published (IARC 1992, UNEP/WHO/ICNIRP 1994, NRPB 1995). The following summary is based principally on these.

Non-melanoma skin cancer

Non-melanoma skin cancer (NMSC) represents around 10% of registered cancers in many European countries, but less than 0.5% of cancer deaths. The majority of NMSC are basal cell carcinomas (BCC) and the remainder squamous cell carcinomas (SCC). Epidemiological data indicate that the main causal factor for NMSC is solar radiation exposure and that the risk is related to cumulative solar radiation exposure. The trends of incidence of NMSC with time are difficult to determine, principally because reliably complete registration of the disease has not been achieved. However, specific survey studies carried out in the USA, Australia and Canada indicate that between the 1960s and the 1980s the prevalence of NMSC has increased in these countries (Fears and Scotto 1982, Glass and Hoover 1989, Marks *et al* 1993 and Gallacher *et al* 1990).

The risk of NMSC has been examined in respect of a number of different personal and exposure characteristics and the following summarises some of the conclusions related to these.

Phenotype NMSC is more prevalent among whites than among blacks (Scotto *et al* 1983). Among whites, personal characteristics indicating a raised risk of NMSC are blue eyes, pale skin, blond or red hair, a tendency to sunburn easily, freckling, the presence of a large number of solar keratoses and an inability to tan in the sun (Green *et al* 1988 and Kricker *et al* 1991).

Anatomical site The anatomical distribution of NMSC correlates to body sites most commonly exposed to solar radiation. Studies indicate that the majority of these cancers occur on the head and neck, although recently published Australian data indicate the proportion may be only around 50% or less (Giles *et al* 1988, Kricker *et al* 1990). The correlation between cancer site and sun-exposed body areas is strong for SCC but not for BCC. Appreciable proportions of SCC occur on the face, forearms, hands, legs and feet.

Gender Among whites, NMSC is more common in men than in women.

Geographical location Annual incidence rates of NMSC appear to show little correlation with latitude as indicated by data on skin cancer incidence in 29 populations of mainly European origin in five continents (UNEP/WHO/ICNIRP 1994). However, within individual countries there is a clearer relationship between increased incidence of NMSC with decreasing latitude (for example, Scotto *et al* 1974 for the USA and Marks *et al* 1993 for Australia). In Australia the incidence of NMSC in migrants to the country most of whom were born in Britain is approximately one-half of the incidence among those born in Australia (Armstrong *et al* 1983, Giles *et al* 1988). These data indicate that early exposure or cumulative exposure are important factors in risk.

Personal exposure to solar radiation Epidemiological studies have been carried out addressing links between risk and personal exposure to solar radiation (IARC 1992). These have relied on assessments of personal exposure perhaps stretching back over decades. These are likely to be subject to error as they are based on personal recollections of events such as episodes of sun exposure or of sunburns many years previously. Such recollections may be subject to recall bias. Generally the results of these studies have indicated that there is a greater risk in relation to greater exposure to solar radiation. However, two studies, using a more quantitative measure of personal solar radiation exposure have found no consistent evidence of a positive correlation of risk for both BCC and SCC subtypes of NMSC with exposure (Vitasa *et al* 1990). Conflicting results are indicated in two recent studies based on history of sunburn. Whereas an increasing risk in BCC was indicated in a study carried out by Hunter *et al* (1990), no such increase was noted in a study by Green and Battistutta (1990). This latter study did however indicate an increased risk in SCC with increased numbers of painful sunburns (UNEP/WHO/ICNIRP 1994).

Although early clinical reports indicated an association between risk of NMSC and outdoor occupations (For example, Blum 1948, Emmett 1973), the epidemiological evidence for an association is weak (UNEP/WHO/ICNIRP 1994). Well conducted studies using exposure classification based on job title have found only small differences in risk between outdoor and indoor workers. Several studies on populations have reported associations between risk and employment in agriculture and outdoor employment generally but interpretation of the results is complicated for various reasons (UNEP/WHO/ICNIRP 1994).

Personal exposure to artificial sources of UVR The use of sunlamps has been associated with a statistically significant increased risk of SCC (Aubry and MacGibbon 1985) but other studies found no such association with the use of sunlamps or sunbeds (O'Loughlin *et al* 1985, Herity *et al* 1989, Hogan *et al* 1989).

Medical exposures

Several studies have been carried out to investigate the risk of NMSC in relation to medical exposures from ultraviolet radiation. One case-control study (Stern *et al* 1980) found a raised risk associated with extensive treatment with topical application of coal tar and/or UVR exposure. However, the significance of these results with respect to UVR exposure alone remains unclear because of the potential for confounding by Psoralen UVA (PUVA) exposure. Patients suffering from psoriasis have been treated by PUVA since the mid-1970s and several studies have demonstrated increased risk of NMSC in such patients. These patients may also receive other potentially carcinogenic treatments and psoriasis itself may be associated with a risk of skin cancer, so these results should be interpreted with caution. However, several studies have indicated a strong dose-response relationship between cumulative PUVA exposure and the risk of SCC and, in one study, a weaker dose-response relationship with BCC (Stern *et al* 1988, Forman *et al* 1989) which appears to be inexplicable in relation to exposure to other carcinogenic agents.

Malignant melanoma

Malignant melanoma (MM), although far less prevalent than NMSC, is the major cause of death from skin cancer and represents an important public health issue for white populations in all European countries. It has become one of the most common cancers in young white adults, its incidence having risen steadily over several decades. It now represents about 8% of cancers in the 20 to 40 years age group and about 4% of deaths in this group in many European countries.

Malignant melanoma has been much more likely to be reported and accurately diagnosed than non-melanoma skin cancers and has been better studied epidemiologically. Around 30 case-control epidemiological studies have indicated a number of correlations between the genetic and personal characteristics and behaviour of people, estimates of their solar radiation exposure and risk of malignant melanoma. These include:

Phenotype The strongest risk factor yet found for MM in whites is a large number of atypical naevi (moles) (Elwood *et al* 1990). There is evidence that solar radiation exposure early in life may be an aetiological factor in the development of such naevi. Blue eyes, red or fair hair and pale complexion are well-established risk factors for MM in people of European origin (for example, Elwood *et al* 1984, Holman and Armstrong 1984). There are also correlations between an inability to tan, an increased tendency to sunburn and a tendency to freckle and the risk of MM. Experimental studies have demonstrated a lower minimum erythemal dose and more prolonged erythema persistence in melanoma patients than in controls.

Anatomical site For whites, MM occurs less frequently on body sites usually unexposed to solar radiation than on sites regularly or intermittently exposed. The most common site for MM in men is the trunk and in women the lower limbs. The large proportion of MM on normally intermittently exposed body parts has been construed as evidence for an association between intermittent exposure to solar radiation and risk of MM. This is supported by the observation that the trunk and the limbs, not normally exposed to solar radiation, receive a higher exposure during sunbathing (or swimming) than when the person is standing. There is, however, evidence to support the hypothesis that exposure on any body site may increase the risk of MM occurring on even an unexposed site by means of systemic effects. It has been found experimentally that UVR exposure in humans can cause proliferation of melanocytes in parts of the body not exposed to the radiation (Stierner *et al* 1989). Additionally, if the occurrence of MM is quantified in terms of unit area of exposed site then the occurrence on the face is relatively high implying the importance also of cumulative solar radiation exposure.

Gender In most white populations, for people under age 60 years, the incidence of MM is higher in women than in men. Above that age the incidences are broadly similar. There is a greater occurrence of MM on the back in men than in women and on the lower limbs in women than in men. Evidence to further support exposure to solar radiation in the aetiology of MM comes from the observation that there is a significantly greater male to female incidence ratio for the scalp and often for the ears than for the face and the greater female to male ratio for the leg than for the thigh and foot.

Geographical location The incidence of MM in white populations generally increases with decreasing latitude. The greatest recorded incidence is in Queensland, Australia where the annual rates are 10 times in women and over 20 times in men the rates in Europe (39 per 10^5 in women and 49 per 10^5 in men (MacLennan *et al* 1992). Lowest rates are reported in parts of Asia (0.7 per 10^5 per annum (UNEP/WHO/ICNIRP 1994)). Studies carried out in the USA indicate good correlations between MM rates and measured or estimated solar UVR levels (Scotto and Fears 1987). However, across Europe the picture is somewhat more complicated, the rates being higher in Scotland and Scandinavia and lower around the Mediterranean. It has been suggested that the latitude gradient in peoples' pigmentation and northern Europeans taking sun-holidays further south may contribute to this.

Personal exposure to solar radiation A number of indices of personal solar radiation exposure have been examined with respect to the risk of MM.

A number of epidemiological studies have examined risk in relation to history of sunburn and generally have indicated a moderate to strong statistical association (for example, IARC 1992). Positive associations have been demonstrated for both sunburn in childhood and sunburn at any age. However, it is not clear whether these data indicate a direct association with sunburn *per se* or the fact that sunburn is an indicator of personal solar radiation exposure (UNEP/WHO/ICNIRP 1994). Additionally, skin sensitivity is clearly important in relation to sunburn and in some cases this makes interpretation of studies difficult.

Other studies have assessed sun exposure by personal recollections of time spent out of doors in work, recreation and vacations and type of clothing worn. There is, however, potential for misclassification in lifetime recall of these and other factors.

In respect of cumulative exposure to solar radiation as a significant risk factor in the aetiology of MM, the evidence is equivocal. Several studies have indicated no significant relationships, while others have been contradictory. However, the risk of MM has been shown to be increased in people with a previous history of NMSC and of solar keratoses, both of which are biological indicators of cumulative solar radiation exposure (UNEP/WHO/ICNIRP 1994).

The results of case-control studies examining the relationship between intermittent solar radiation exposure and MM risk have generally been positive. These have examined indices of intermittent exposure including activities such as sunbathing, sailing and holidays in sunny climes or overall recreational exposures. A case-control study carried out in Western Australia (Holman and Armstrong 1984) showed a substantially higher risk of MM in native born Australians than in migrants to the State after the age of 15 years. This implies that exposure early in life may be important to risk. A similar difference in risk was also demonstrated in a New Zealand study (Cooke and Fraser 1985).

Personal exposure to artificial sources of UVR Several studies have reported increased risk of MM in users of sunlamps and sunbeds (IARC 1992) but others have not. Most studies did not adjust for solar radiation exposure, which is a potential confounder.

A study by Beral (Beral *et al* 1982) indicated an increased risk of MM associated with the use of fluorescent lamps. Since then several other studies have been carried out. The results have been inconsistent and overall do not support an effect (IARC 1992). Other studies have examined associations between exposure to different sources of UVR and the risk of MM. These include the use of UVR-emitting lamps for printing, laboratory equipment, insect lures, black lights and photocopiers. An Australian study (Holman *et al* 1986) found no correlation between exposure and risk while a Canadian study (Elwood *et al* 1986) found a borderline significant risk for MM in a similar study that additionally included arc welding. Another Canadian study found no significant increase in risk associated with either arc welding or any other occupational exposure to UVR (Siemiatycik 1991).

Other cancers

Cancer of the lip Cancers of the lip occur most frequently on the lower lip which supports the aetiology with solar radiation exposure. The incidence is greater in men than in women and is greater in whites than in blacks and increases rapidly with age. Studies have demonstrated greater risks for outdoor workers compared with indoor workers and higher risks for native born people in Australia and Israel compared with those for migrants to these countries. These observations again support the aetiology with solar radiation exposure.

Ocular malignant melanoma The association between the risk of ocular and exposure to solar radiation is inconclusive. Case-control studies have shown an increased risk of ocular MM for individuals with blue eyes, fair or red hair, and having skins with a tendency to freckle, sunburn readily and not tan. However, neither results for intermittent nor for cumulative exposure indices for solar radiation have been conclusive (for example, Gallacher *et al* 1985, Holly *et al* 1990, Seddon *et al* 1990). There is also some evidence, from some of these studies, of associations between exposure to sunlamps and some other artificial sources of UVR and ocular MM risk.

Cataract There is biological evidence for suspecting exposure to UVR as a risk factor in the development of human cataract. *In vivo* and *in vitro* laboratory studies have demonstrated cataractogenic effects induced by UVR in the wavelength range 300 to 400 nm (Marshall 1991).

The most comprehensive case-control study of cataract risk and UVR exposure was carried out on 838 watermen aged 30 years or greater who worked on Chesapeake Bay, Maryland (Taylor *et al* 1988). The exposure assessment was carried out by calculations based on a detailed history of occupational and leisure exposure, eyewear worn, hat use and arc welding use, together with laboratory and field measurements of ambient solar ultraviolet radiation combined with exposure geometry considerations. The exposure assessment thus included estimated annual exposure for each year of life to UVB and to UVA. The prevalence of cortical and nuclear cataracts was found to increase with age which is compatible with the risk being associated with cumulative exposure to solar radiation. The prevalence of cortical cataract was significantly associated with UVB exposure but the prevalence of nuclear cataract was not. The relative risk for cortical cataract was 3.3 times higher in the highest exposed group compared with the lowest.

The results of geographical studies have often been difficult to interpret but overall lend support to exposure to solar radiation in the aetiology of cataract (for example, van Heyningen 1975, Taylor 1980, Hollows and Moran 1981, Brilliant *et al* 1983, Hiller *et al* 1983, 1986).

5.4.2 Visible and infrared radiation

Visible radiation

The principal concern with respect to exposure to visible radiation relates to retinal injury and particularly to photochemical damage to the photoreceptors of the retina (so-called blue-light damage). In normal eyes the retina receives little exposure to UVA radiation after childhood as by this time the transmission of the intervening ocular media is very low. Deliberately staring at the sun will cause retinal injury, which in the absence of magnification from, for example, using binoculars, will be photochemical injury caused by blue light.

Infrared radiation

The organs considered to be at risk from exposure to IRR are the skin and the eyes. In the case of the skin, except for possible injury from medical and high power industrial lasers, the risks are limited to flash burns (Sliney and Wolbarsht 1980). However most industrial sources do not emit sufficient power to cause injury in times shorter than the normal protective reaction time. In domestic and public places the probability of injuries, to the skin, from IRR exposure is small, except from large scale conflagrations affecting buildings and transportation vehicles. Even in these cases the injuries are normally the result of heat conduction and not radiation.

The parts of the eye most at risk are the cornea, lens and the retina. In the case of the cornea the reaction time is comparable to that for skin and except for flash burns and exposure to laser emissions injury is similarly unlikely.

Epidemiological data have been limited to studies on the incidence of cataracts in industrial workers.

Lydahl and Philipson (1984), in a study of iron and steel workers, found an increase prevalence of senile lens opacities in elderly IRR-exposed workers. A similar study by the same authors, of workers employed in the Swedish manual glass industry again indicated an increased risk (for cataract) and recommended the wearing of protective eye-wear.

Dunn (1950) in a study of medical and compensation records from 1921 to 1950 found no cases of cataract in glass workers.

Minton (1949) discussed the incidence of lenticular and retinal injuries to workers in the metal production industry and among electric and gas welders. This is largely a qualitative discussion but includes some numerical data.

A paper by Grant-Peterkin (1955) discussed cases of association between *ab igne* (a chronic inflammation of the skin following prolonged exposure to IRR) and the onset of squamous cell skin cancer.

5.5   Summary

5.5.1   Time varying electromagnetic fields of frequencies less than 100 kHz

A large number of epidemiological studies have been conducted in recent years concerning cancer in relation to exposure to electromagnetic fields. Greatest attention has been given to studies of childhood cancer in relation to residential exposures. Three studies conducted in Nordic countries were well controlled and substantially better than those (principally in the USA) that previously reported associations with childhood cancer. These studies do not establish that exposure to electromagnetic fields is a cause of cancer. Although, taken together, they provide some evidence to suggest that the possibility exists in the case of childhood leukaemia, the number of affected children in these studies is very small. Some recent occupational studies have strengthened the evidence for believing that some groups of workers in industries where exposure to electromagnetic fields may have been particularly elevated have had an increased risk of leukaemia, but not of brain cancer. However, the occupational studies are neither consistent in the type of leukaemia found to be increased nor consistent in finding a progressive increase with increasing exposure.

5.5.2   Electromagnetic fields and radiation of frequencies between 100 kHz and 300 GHz

Available epidemiological data are scarce and inconclusive and do not prove any cause-effect relationship between exposure and the development of cancer. They indicate, however, that the cancer risk associated with electromagnetic fields, if any, is very small. More research is needed to improve the epidemiological data base, and to test the biological plausibility of the hypothesised link between RF/MW fields and cancer.

5.5.3   Optical radiation

The evidence overall, both from descriptive and analytic epidemiology, strongly supports the notion that non-melanoma skin cancer aetiology is related to cumulative dose of solar radiation exposure. No competing hypothesis has been put forward which would satisfactorily explain the site distribution of these tumours, mainly on permanently exposed body sites, the increasing incidence with age, and the findings from person-based epidemiological studies. The findings from geographical studies, from the anatomical site distributions of the tumours, and from person-based epidemiology, suggest that SCC is more strongly related to UVR exposure than is BCC. Data from patients treated with PUVA show a strong dose-response relationship of the treatment to SCC risk and far less to BCC risk, although as yet the separate contributions of psoralen administration and UVA have not been established.

Risk of cutaneous melanoma is increasing in white populations and the major risk factor appears to be exposure to solar radiation. While cumulative exposure to this factor is probably the main cause of melanomas of the head and neck and although there are insufficient data to assess the relationship of melanoma of unexposed sites to sun radiation exposure, intense short-term exposures of untanned skin appear likely to be the main cause of melanoma of intermittently exposed skin sites. There is also evidence, particularly from data on migrants and recall of sunburn history, that exposures in childhood and adolescence may be of special importance to risk of melanoma. Several of the results on this issue, however, are potentially biased, and therefore the relationship is still uncertain. The strongest personal risk factor yet found for MM in whites is a large number of moles.

121

Overall, the data for cataract suggest, although with less certainty than for non-melanoma skin cancer, that cumulative UVR exposure is important to the aetiology of at least cortical cataracts. Since the most convincing evidence has come from highly exposed men, and since the gradient of risk with latitude in the general population (in the USA) appears to be relatively small, it is unclear to what extent UVR is a risk factor for cataracts in the general population in western countries.

References

Ahlbom, A, Feychting, M, Koskenvuo, M, Olsen, J H, Pukkala, E, Schulgen, G, and Verkasalo, P. 1993. Electromagnetic fields and childhood cancer (letter). *Lancet*, **342**, 1295–1296.

Armstrong, B K, Woodings, T L, Stenhouse, N S, and McColl, M G. 1983. *Mortality from cancer in migrants to Australia, 1962 to 1971*. Perth, University of Western Australia, 21 and 81–83.

Aubry, F, and MacGibbon, B. 1985. Risk factors of squamous cell carcinoma of the skin. A case control study in the Montreal region. *Cancer*, **55**, 907–911.

Baroncelli, P, Battisti, S, Checcucci, A, Comba, P, Grandolfo, M, Serio, A, and Vecchia, P, 1986. A health examination of railway high-voltage substation workers exposed to ELF electromagnetic fields. *Am. J. Ind. Med.*, **10**, 45–55.

Beral, V, Evans, S, Shaw, H, and Milton, G. 1982. Malignant melonoma and exposure to fluorescent lighting at work. *Lancet*, ii, 290–293.

Blum, H F. 1948. Sunlight as a casual factor in cancer of the skin in man. *J. Natl. Inst. Cancer*, **9**, 247–258.

Brilliant, L B, Grasset, N C, Pokkrel, R P, et al. 1983. Associations among cataract prevalence, sunlight hours, and altitude in the Himalayas. *Am. J. Epidemiol.*, **118**, 250–264.

Broadbent, D E, Broadbent, M H, Male J C, and Jones, M R L, 1985. Health of workers exposed to electric fields. *Br. J. Ind. Med.*, **42**, 75–84.

Cartwright, R A. 1993. Magnetic fields and childhood cancer. IN *Medizinische Forschung 6*. Stuttgart, New York and Jena, Gustav Fischer Verlag, pp 115–128.

Coleman, M, and Beral, V. 1988. A review of epidemiological studies of the health effects of living near or working with electricity generation and transmission equipment. *Int. J. Epidemiol.*, **17**.

Coleman, M P, Bell, C M J, Tayler, H-L, and Primic-Zakelj, M. 1989. Leukaemia and residence near electricity transmission equipment: A case-control study. *Br. J. Cancer*, **60**, 793–798.

Cooke, K R, and Fraser, J. 1985. Migration and death from malignant melanoma. *Int. J. Cancer*, **36**, 175–178.

DMH. 1994. Report on the risk of cancer in children living in homes exposed to 50 Hz magnetic fields from high-voltage lines. Copenhagen, National Board of Health, Statens Information.

Dennis, J A, Muirhead, C R, and Ennis, J R. 1992. Human health and exposure to electromagnetic radiations. Chilton, NRPB-R241. London, HMSO.

Dunn, K L. 1950. Cataract from infra-red rays (glass workers cataract). *Arch. Ind. Hyg. Occup. Med.*, **1**, 166–180.

Elwood, J M, Gallocher, R P, Hill, G B, Spirelli, J J, Pearson, J C G, and Threfall, W. 1984. Pigmentation and skin reactions to sun as risk factors for cutaneous melonoma: Western Canada Melonoma Study. *Br. Med. J.*, **288**, 99–102.

Elwood, J M, Williamson, C, and Stapleton, C J. 1986. Malignant melanoma in relation to moles, pigmentation and exposure to fluorescent and other lighting sources. *Br. J. Cancer*, **53**, 65–74.

Elwood, J M, Whitehead, S M, Davison, J, Stewart, M, and Galt, M. 1990. Malignant melanoma in England: risk associated with naevi, freckles, social class, hair colour, and sunburn. *Int. J. Epidemiol.* **19**, 801–810.

Emmett, E A. 1973. Ultraviolet radiation as a cause of skin tumours. *Crit. Rev. Toxicol.*, **2**, 211–255.

EPRI. 1989. Extremely low frequency electric and magnetic fields and cancer: A literature review. Palo Alto, Electric Power Research Institute. Report No. EPRI EN-6674.

Fears, T R, and Scotto, J. 1982. Changes in skin cancer morbidity between 1971-72 and 1977-78. *J. Natl Cancer Inst.*, **69**, 365–370.

Feychting, M, and Ahlbom, A. 1993. Magnetic fields and cancer in children residing near Swedish high-voltage power lines. *Am. J. Epidemiol.*, **138**, 467–481.

Floderus, B, Persson, T, Stenlund, C, Wennberg, A, Öst, A, and Knave, B. 1993. Occupational exposure to electromagnetic fields in relation to leukaemia and brain tumours: A case-control study in Sweden. *Cancer Causes Control*, **4**, 465–476.

Forman, A B, Roenigk, H H, Caro, W A, and Magio, M L. 1989. Long-term follow-up of skin cancer in the PUVA-48 cooperative study. *Arch. Dermatol.*, **125**, 515–519.

Fulton, J P, Cobb, S, Preble, L, Leone, L, and Forman, E. 1980. Electrical wiring configurations and childhood leukaemia in Rhode Island. *Am. J. Epidemiol.*, **111**, 292–296.

Gallacher, R P, Elwood, J M, Rootman, J, Spirelli, J J, Hill, G B, Threfall, W J, and Birdsell J M. 1985. Risk factors for ocular melonoma: Western Canada Melanoma Study. *J. Natl Cancer, Inst.*, **74**, 775–778.

Gallacher, R P, Ma, B, McLean, D I. 1990. Trends in basal cell carcinoma, squamous cell carcinoma and melanoma of the skin from 1973 through 1987. *J. Am. Acad. Dermatol.*, **23**, 413–421.

Gamberale, F, Anshelm Olson, B, Eneroth, P, Lindh, T, and Wennberg, A. 1989. Acute effects of ELF electromagnetic fields: A study of linesmen working with 400 kV power lines. *Br. J. Ind. Med.*, **46**, 729–737.

Giles, G G, Marks, R, and Foley, P. 1988. Incidence of non-melanocytic skin cancer treated in Australia. *Br. Med. J.*, **296**, 13–17.

Glass, A G, and Hoover, R N. 1989. The enlarging epidemic of melanoma and squamous cell skin cancer. *J. Am. Med. Assoc.*, **262**, 2097–2100.

Graham, R B. 1985. The medical results of human exposure to radiofrequency radiation. IN *The impact of proposed radio frequency radiation standards on military operations*. Neuilly-sur-Seine, France Advisory Group for Aerospace Research and Development (AGARD) (Lecture Series No. 138), 6.1 – 6.8.

Grandolfo, M, Vecchia, P, Comba, P. 1989. Linee ad alta tensione: modalità di esposizione e valutazione del rischio sanitario. *Rapporti Istisan 80/20.* (In Italian).

Grant-Peterkin, G A. 1955. Malignant change in erythema *ab igne*. *Br. Med. J.*, December 31, 1599–1602.

Green, A C, and Battistutta, D. 1990. Incidence and determinants of skin cancer in a high-risk Australian population. *Int. J. Cancer*, **46**, 356–361.

Green, A C, Beardmore, G, Hart, V, Leslie, D, Marko, R, and Staines, D. 1988. Skin cancer in a Queensland population. *J. Am. Acad. Dermatol.*, **19**, 1045–1052.

Hamnerius, Y, Agrip, G, Galt, S, Nilsson, R, Sandblom, J, and Lindgren, R. 1993. Provocation study of reaction associated with exposure to electromagnetic fields from VDUs. IN Transactions of the 2nd Congress of the European Bioelectromagnetics Association. Bled. Slovenia, December, pp 8–9.

Herity, B, O'Loughlin, C, Moriarty, M J, and Conroy, R. 1989. Risk factors for non-melonoma skin cancer. *Irish Med. J.*, **82**, 151–152.

Hiller, R, Sperduto, R D, and Ederer, F. 1983. Epidemiologic associations with cataract in the 1971–72 National Health and Nutrition Examination Study. *Am. J. Epidemiol.*, **118**, 239–249.

Hiller, R, Sperduto, R D, and Ederer, F. 1986. Epidemiologic associations with nuclear, cortical and postsubcapsulor cataracts. *Am. J. Epidemiol.*, **126**, 916–925.

Hogan, D J, To, T, Gran, L, Wong, D, and Lane, P R. 1989. Risk factors for basal cell carcinoma. *Int. J. Dermatol.*, **28**, 591–594.

Hollows, F, and Moran, D. 1981. Cataract – the ultraviolet risk factor. *Lancet*, **2**, 1249–1250.

Holly, E A, Aston, D A, Char, D H, Kristiansen, J J, and Ahn, D K. 1990. Uveal melanoma in relation to ultraviolet light exposure and host factors. *Cancer Res.*, **50**, 5773–5777.

Holman, C D J, and Armstrong, B K. 1984. Pigmentary traits, ethnic origin, benign nevi, and family history as risk factors for cutaneous malignant melanoma. *J. Natl Cancer Inst.*, **72**, 257–266.

Holman, C D J, Armstong, B K, Heenan, P J, Blackwell, J B, Cumming, F J, English, D R, Holland S, Kelsall, G R H, Matz, L R, Rouse, I L, Singh, A, Ten Seldam, R E J, Watt, J D and Xu, J. 1986. The causes of malignant melanoma: results from the West Australian Lions Melanoma Research Project. *Recent Results cancer Res.*, **102**, 18–37.

Hunter, D J, Colditz, G A, Stampfer, M J, Rosner, B, Willet, W S, and Speizer, F E. 1990. Risk factors for basal cell carcinoma in a prospective cohort of women. *Ann. Epidemiology*, **1**, 13–23.

IARC. 1992. Solar and ultraviolet radiation. IARC Monograph on the evaluation of carcinogenic risks to humans, Volume 55. Lyon, International Agency for Research on Cancer.

IRPA/INIRC 1990. Interim guidelines on limits of exposure to 50/60 Hz electric and magnetic fields. *Health Phys.*, **58**, 113–122.

John, E M, Savitz, D A, and Sandler, D P. 1991. Prenatal exposure to parents' smoking and childhood cancer. *Am. J. Epidemiol.*, **133**, 123.

Knave, B, Gamberale, F, Bergstrom, S, Birke, E, Iregren, A, Kolmodin-Hedman, B, and Wennberg, A. 1979. Long-term exposure to electric fields. A cross-sectional epidemiological investigation on occupationally-exposed high-voltage substations. *Scand. J. Work Environ. Health*, **5**, 115–125.

Kricker, A, English, D R, Randell, P L, Heenan, P J, Clay, C D, Delaney, T A, and Armstrong, B K. 1990. Skin cancer in Geraldton, Western Australia: A summary of incidence and prevalence. *Med. J. Aust.*, **152**, 399–407.

Kricker, A, Armstrong, B K, English, D R, and Heenan, P J. 1991. Pigmentary and cutaneous risk factors for non-melanocytic skin cancer: A case control study. *Int. J. Cancer*, **48**, 650–662.

Larsen, AL, Olsen, J, and Svane, O. 1991. Gender-specific reproductive outcome and exposure to high-frequency electromagnetic radiation among physiotherapists. *Scand. J. Work. Environ. Health*, **16**, 324–329.

Lillienfeld, A M, Tonascia, J, Tonascia, S, Libauer, C A, and Cauthen, G M. 1978. Foreign service health status study - evaluation of health status of foreign service and other employees from selected eastern European posts Final report, Washington, DC, Department of State, pp 436. (Contract No. 6025-619073 (NTIS PB-288163), p 436.

Lin, S R, and Lu, P Y. 1989. An epidemiological study of childhood cancer in relation to residential exposure to electromagnetic fields. Abstract from DOE/EPRI "Contractors" meeting, Portland, Oregon.

London, S J, Thomas, D C, Browman, J D, Sobel, E, Cheng, T-C, and Peters, J M. 1991. Exposure to residential electric and magnetic fields and risk of childhood leukaemia. *Am. J. Epidemiol.,* **134,** 923–937.

Lydahl, E. and Philipson B. 1984. Infrared Radiation and Cataract. *ACTA Ophthalmol. Supplementum 166,* ii:1 - ii:22; and iv:1 – iv:29.

MacLennan, R, Green, A C, McLeod, G R C, and Martin, N G. 1992. Increasing incidence of cutaneous melonoma in Queensland, Australia. *J. Natl Cancer Inst.,* **84,** 1427–1432.

Malboysson, E, 1976. Medical control of men working within electric fields. *Rev. Gen. Electr.,* Numero special (juillet), 75–80.

Marcus, M. 1990. Epidemiologic studies of VDT use and pregnancy outcome. *Reprod. Toxicol.,* **4,** 51–56.

Marks, R, Staples, M, and Giles, G G. 1993. Trends in non-melanocytic skin cancer treated in Australia: The second National Survey. *Int. J. Cancer,* **53,** 585–590.

Marshall, J. 1991. The effects of ultraviolet radiation and blue light on the eye. IN *The Susceptible Visual Apparatus,* Volume 16 of *Vision and Visual Dysfunction.* (Cronly-Dillon, J R, (ed). London, MacMillan Press.

Matanoski, G M, Breysse, P N, and Elliott, E A. 1991. Electromagnetic field exposure and male breast cancer. *Lancet,* **337,** 737.

McDowell, M E. 1986. Mortality of persons resident in the vicinity of electricity transmission facilities. *Br. J. Cancer,* **53,** 271.

Milham, S Jr. 1988. Increased mortality in amateur radio operators due to lymphatic and hematopoietic malignancies. *Am. J. Epidemiol.,* **127,** 50–54.

Minton, J. 1949. Occupational diseases of the lens and retina. *Bri. Med. J.,* March 5, 392–394.

Muhm. 1992. Mortality investigations of workers on electromagnetic pulse test program. *J. Occup. Med.,* **34,** 287–292.

Myers, A, Clayden, A D, Cartwright, R A, and Cartwright, S C. 1990. Childhood cancer and overhead powerlines: A case-control study. *Br. J. Cancer,* **62,** 1008–1014.

NRPB. 1992. Electromagnetic fields and the risk of cancer. Report of an Advisory Group on Non-ionising Radiation. *Doc. NRPB,* **3,** No. 1, 1–138.

NRPB. 1993. Electromagnetic fields and the risk of cancer. Summary of the views of the Advisory Group on Non-ionising Radiation on epidemiological studies published since its 1992 report. *Doc. NRPB,* **4,** No. 5, 65–9.

NRPB. 1994a. Electromagnetic fields and the risk of cancer. Supplementary report by the Advisory Group on Non-ionising Radiation of 12 April 1994. *Radiol. Prot. Bull.* No. 154, 10–12.

NRPB. 1994b. Health effects related to the use of visual display units. Report of an Advisory Group on Non-ionising Radiation. *Doc. NRPB,* **5,** No. 2, 1–75.

NRPB. 1995. The health effects of ultraviolet radiation. Report of an Advisory Group on Non-ionising Radiation. In press.

O'Loughlin, C, Moriarty, M J, Herity, B, and Daly, L. 1985. A re-appraisal of risk factors for skin carcinoma in Ireland: A case control study. *Irish J. Med. Sci.,* **154,** 61–65.

Olsen, J H, Nielsen, A, and Schulgen, G. 1993. Residence near high voltage facilities and risk of cancer in children. *Br. Med. J.,* **307,** 891–895.

ORAU. 1992. Health effects of low-frequency electric and magnetic fields. Report prepared by an Oak Ridge Associated Universities panel for the Committee on Interagency Radiation Research and Policy Coordination. Oak Ridge, ORAU 92/F9.

Ouellet-Hellstrom, R, and Stewart, W F. 1993. Miscarriages among female physical therapists who report using radio- and microwave-frequency electromagnetic radiation. *Am. J. Epidemiol.*, **138**, 775–786.

Roberge, P F. 1976. Study on the state of health of electrical maintenance workers on Hydro-Quebec 735 kV power transmission system. Montreal, Report of Health Department, Hydro-Quebec.

Robinette, C D, Silverman, C, and Jablon, S. 1980. Effects upon health of occupational exposure to microwave radiation (radar). *Am. J. Epidemiol.*, **112**, 39–53.

Sahl, J D, Kelso, M A and Greenland, S. 1993. Cohort and nested case-control studies of haematopoietic cancers and brain cancer among electricity utility workers. *Epidemiology*, **4**, 104–114.

Savitz, D A. 1993. Overview of epidemiological research on electric and magnetic fields and cancer. *Am. Ind. Hyg. Assoc. J.*, **54**, 197–204.

Savitz, D A, and Feingold, L. 1989. Association of childhood cancer with residential traffic density. *Scand. J. Work Environ. Health*, **15**, 360.

Savitz, D A, Wachtel, H, Barnes, F A, John, E M and Tvrdick, J G. 1988. Case-control study of childhood cancer and exposure to 60-Hz magnetic fields. *Am. J. Epidemiol.*, **128**, 21-36.

Savitz, D A, John, E M, and Kleckner, R C. 1990. Magnetic field exposure from electric appliances and childhood cancer. *Am. J. Epidemiol.*, **131**, 763-73.

Scotto, J, Fears, T R, and Fraumeni, J F Jnr. 1983. *Incidence of non melanoma skin cancer in the United States.* Bethesda MD, Natural Cancer Institute, NIH Publication No. 83-2433.

Scotto, J, and Fears, T R. 1987. The association of solar ultraviolet and skin melanoma incidence among Caucasians in the United States. *Cancer Invest.*, **5**, 275–283.

Scotto, J, Kopf, A W, and Urbach, F. 1974. Non-melanoma skin cancer among Caucasians in four areas of the United States. *Cancer*, **34**, 1333–1338.

Seddon, J M, Gragoudas, E S, Glynn, R J, Egan, K M, Albert, D M, and Blitzer, P H. 1990. Host factors, UV radiation and the risk of uveal melanoma. A case-control study. *Arch. Ophthalmol.*, **108**, 1274–1280.

Severson, R K, Stevens, R G, Kaüne, W T, Thomas, D B, Heuser, L, Davis, S, and Sever, L E. 1988. Acute nonlymphocytic leukaemia and residential exposure to power frequency magnetic fields. *Am. J. Epidemiol.*, **128**, 10.

Siemiatycik, J. 1991. *Risk Factors for Cancer in the Workplace.* Boca Raton, CRC Press.

Silva, J M, Hammon, N P, Huber, D L, Zaffanella, L E, and Deno, D W, 1985. AC field exposure study: Human exposure to 60 Hz electric fields. Palo Alto, Electrical Power Research Institute, Interim report EA-3993, Research Project 799-16.

Singewald, M L, Langworthy, O R, and Kouwenhoven, W B, 1973. Medical follow-up study of HV linemen working in AC electric fields. *IEEE Trans. Power Appl. Syst.*, **PAS-92**, 1307–1309.

Sliney, D H, and Wolbarsht, M. 1980. *Safety with Lasers and Other Optical Sources.* New York and London, Plenum Press, p 162.

Stern, R S, Lange, R, and members of the Photochemotherapy Follow-up Study. 1988. Non-melanoma skin cancer occurring in patients treated with PUVA five to ten years after first treatment. *J. Invest. Dermatol.*, **91**, 120–124.

Stern, R S, Zierler, S, and Parrish, S. 1980. Skin carcinoma in patients with psoriasis treated with topical tar and artificial ultraviolet radiation. *Lancet*, i, 732–735.

Stevens, R G. 1987. Electric power use and breast cancer: A hypothesis. *Am. J. Epidemiol.*, **125**, 556.

Stierner, U, Rosdahl, I, Augustsson A and Kogedahl, B, 1989. UVB irradiation incides melamocyte increase in both exposed and shielded human skin. *J. Invest. Dermatol.*, **92**, 561–564.

Stopps, G J, and Janischewsky, W, 1979. Epidemiological study of workers maintaining HV equipment and transmission lines in Ontario. Vancouver, Canadian Electrical Association.

Strumza, M V. 1970. Influence sur la santé humaine de la proximité des conducteurs de l'electricité a haute tension. *Arch. Mal. Prof.*, **31**, 269–276.

Taylor, H R. 1980. The environment and the lens. *Br. J. Ophthalmol.*, **64**, 303–310.

Taylor, H R, West, S K, Rosenthol, F S, Minoz, B, Newland, H S, Abbey, H, and Emmett, E A. 1988. Effect of ultraviolet radiation on cataract formation. *New Eng. J. Med.*, **319**, 1429–1433.

Thériault, G, Goldberg, M, Miller, A B, Amstrong, B, Guénel, P, Deadman, J, Imbernon, E, To, T, Chevalier, A, Cyr, D, and Wall, C. 1994. Cancer risks associated with occupational exposure to magnetic fields among electric utility workers in Ontario and Quebec, Canada and France: 1970–1989. *Am. J. Epidemiol.*, **139**, 550–572.

Tomenius, L. 1986. 50-Hz electromagnetic environment and the incidence of childhood tumours in Stockholm County. *Bioelectromagnetics*, **7**, 191–207.

Tynes, T, and Anderson, A. 1990. Electromagnetic fields and male breast cancer. *Lancet*, **336**, 1596.

Tynes, T, Anderson, A, and Langmark, F. 1992. Incidence of cancer in Norwegian workers who have been exposed to electromagnetic fields. *Am. J. Epidemiol.*, **136**, 81–88.

Tynes, T, Jynge, H and Vistnes, A I. 1994. Leukaemia and brain tumours in Norwegian railway workers, a nested case-control study. *Am. J. Epidemiol.*, **139**, 645-653.

UNEP/WHO/IRPA. 1984. *Environmental Health Criteria 35 Extremely Low Frequency (ELF) Fields*, Geneva, World Health Organisation.

UNEP/WHO/IRPA. 1987. *Magnetic fields. Environmental Health Criteria 69*, Geneva, World Health Organisation.

UNEP/WHO/IRPA. 1993. *Electromagnetic fields (300 Hz to 300 GHz). Environmental Health Criteria 137*, Geneva, World Health Organisation.

UNEP/WHO/ICNIRP. 1994. *Ultraviolet Radiation. Environmental Health Criteria 160*, Geneva, World Health Organisation.

Verkasalo, P K, Pukkala, E, Hongisto, M Y, Valjus, J E, Järvinen, P J, Heikklilä, K V, and Koskenvuo, M. 1993. Risk of cancer in Finnish children living close to power lines. *Br. Med. J.*, **307**, pp 895-899.

Vitasa, B C, Taylor, H R, Strickland, P T, Rosenthal, F S, West, S, Abbey, H, Ng, S K, Munoz, B, and Emmett, E A. 1990. Association on melanoma skin cancer and actinic keratosis with cumulative solar ultraviolet exposure in Maryland Watermen. *Cancer*, **65**, p 2811–2817.

van Heyingen, R. 1975. What happens to the human lens in cataract. *Sci. Am.*, **223**, 70–81.

Wertheimer, N, and Leeper, E. 1979. Electrical wiring configuration and childhood cancer. *Am. J. Epidemiol.*, **109**, 273–284.

6 Hazard assessment

6.1 Static and slowly time varying fields

6.1.1 Electric fields

Static and extremely slowly time varying electric fields interact with people in two important ways:

- They act on the outer surface of the body. This may be accompanied by hair movement and other sensory stimulation in fields greater than about 10 kV m^{-1} becoming annoying at 25 kV m^{-1}.

- They induce surface charges on conducting objects. Currents may pass through grounded people in contact with such objects.

Field strengths greater than approximately 5–7 kV m^{-1} can produce a wide variety of hazards such as startle reactions associated with spark discharges and contact currents from ungrounded conductors within the field. Care should be taken either to eliminate ungrounded objects, to ground such objects, or to use insulated gloves when ungrounded objects must be handled.

Safety hazards associated with combustion, ignition of flammable materials and electroexplosive devices may exist in the presence of a high intensity electric field.

6.1.2 Magnetic fields

The existing evidence from experiments with laboratory animals indicates an absence of significant effects on many developmental, behavioural, and physiological parameters evaluated at static magnetic flux densities up to 2 T.

According to theoretical considerations, magnetohydrodynamic effects could retard blood flowing in a strong magnetic field and produce a rise in blood pressure. This effect is predicted to cause a flow reduction of at most a few per cent at 5 T, but was not observed at 1.5 T in humans. Current scientific knowledge does not suggest any detrimental effect on major developmental, behavioural, and physiological parameters in higher organisms for transient exposures to static magnetic flux densities up to 2 T.

From the analysis of established mechanisms of interaction, long-term exposure to magnetic flux densities of less than about 200 mT should not have adverse consequences on health.

However, for people with cardiac pacemakers, ferromagnetic implants, and implanted electronic devices there are potential health risks if the magnetic flux density exceeds several mT. The majority of cardiac pacemakers are unlikely to be affected in fields less than 0.5 mT; therefore, cardiac pacemakers and implantable defibrillator bearers should avoid locations where the magnetic flux density exceeds 0.5 mT. There are also other vital electronic aids in increasing use (for example, electronic inner ear prostheses, insulin pumps, electronically guided active prostheses and muscle stimulation devices) that may be susceptible to static magnetic flux densities above a few millitesla, particularly if the person is moving within the field.

People with ferromagnetic implants should consult their physician for advice and, in particular, people with aneurysm clips that are not definitely known to be non-magnetic should not be exposed to magnetic fields above a few mT because of the danger of twisting or dislodgment.

6.2 Time varying electromagnetic fields of frequencies less than 100 kHz

6.2.1 Electric fields

ELF electric fields can be perceived because of the field-induced vibration of body hair, or the occurrence of spark discharges on contact with clothes or grounded objects. The threshold for perception by hair vibration shows wide individual variation. At 50/60 Hz, 50% of all people tested have a perception threshold of 20 kV m^{-1} for sensations from their head hair or tingling between body and clothes. About 90% of the exposed subjects have detection thresholds of greater than 10 to 15 kV m^{-1} at 50/60 Hz, and only 5% are able to detect fields as low as 3 to 5 kV m^{-1}.

Although these effects are not considered to be a hazard, hair vibration and tingling can become an annoyance.

Time varying electric fields, at frequencies below 100 kHz, interact with biological bodies through electrical charges induced on ungrounded metallic objects, such as cars, trucks, cranes, wires, and fences. Two types of interaction may occur:

-    a spark discharge before a person touches the object;

-    the passage of current to ground through a person coming into contact with such an object; the magnitude of the current depends on the total charge on the object and on the person's impedance to ground. The charge, in turn, depends on the frequency and electric field strength, the object geometry and its capacitance.

Above a certain threshold, the current to ground is perceived by the person as a tingling or prickling sensation in the finger or hand touching the charged object, for frequencies below about 100 kHz, and as heat at higher frequencies. A severe shock can be experienced at much higher levels. The threshold currents depend on frequency, surface of contact area, and the individual. Typical threshold values resulting from steady-state contact currents of 50 Hz from different vehicles are 2 to 2.5 kV m^{-1} for the median touch perception for children, finger contact, with a car and 8 to 10 kV m^{-1} for a painful shock for children, finger contact with a truck.

Of greater hazard significance may be the occurrence of capacitive spark discharges (microshocks) which are generated when two objects of different potential come into close proximity and the electric breakdown field strength of the air is exceeded. The current flows across a very small area of skin and results in a high current density which may be perceptible, irritating or painful. Exposed people may demonstrate stress reactions in the presence of repeated spark discharges with increased nervousness and the inability to continue work. The threshold for the perception of spark discharges by 10% of volunteers close to an earthed object has been reported to be 0.6 to 1.5 kV m^{-1} at 50/60 Hz, with a similarly defined threshold for annoyance of 2 to 3.5 kV m^{-1} (UNEP/WHO/IRPA 1984).

Several studies of the incidence of cancer or mortality from cancer among arbitrarily defined occupational groups considered to be exposed to electromagnetic fields (among other factors) suggested an association between electrical occupations and cancer. Because of the inherent uncertainty associated with this type of epidemiological study and the lack of measurement of exposure, no definite conclusion with respect to risk can be drawn.

It has not been established that chronic low-level exposure to electric 50/60 Hz fields increases the risk of cancer.

6.2.2 Magnetic fields

From *in vitro* studies it may be concluded that functions of the central nervous system may be adversely affected by current densities above 10 mA m^{-2} between 10 Hz and 1 kHz and by progressively larger current densities at frequencies above and below this range.

In terms of health risk assessment, it is difficult to correlate precisely tissue current densities with external magnetic flux densities. Assuming appropriate radii for loops in tissue of conductivity 0.2 S m^{-1}, it is possible to calculate the magnetic flux density that would produce potentially hazardous current densities in tissues. The following observations can be made for induced current density ranges and magnetic flux densities of sinusoidal homogeneous fields that produce biological effects from whole-body exposure (UNEP/WHO/IRPA 1987).

- Below 10 mA m^{-2} are the naturally occurring endogenous currents of the body.
- Between 10 and 100 mA m^{-2} there are well-established effects on the visual and nervous system.
- Between 100 and 1000 mA m^{-2} changes in the excitability of nervous tissue is observed and there are possible health hazards.
- Above 1000 mA m^{-2} nerve stimulation and stimulation of the heart including extrasystoles and ventricular fibrillation can occur (acute health hazards).

Several laboratory studies have been conducted on human subjects exposed to sinusoidally time-varying magnetic fields with frequencies of 50/60 Hz. None of these investigations has revealed adverse clinical or significant physiological changes. The strongest magnetic flux density used in these studies with human volunteers was a 5 mT, 50 Hz field to which subjects were exposed for 4 h.

The lowest sensitivity thresholds for magnetophosphenes are about 2 mT at 20 Hz and about 5 mT at 50 Hz.

The threshold value for a malfunction of some sensitive unipolar cardiac pacemakers is 20 µT (50 Hz) under worst case conditions. At about 200 µT most of the implanted pacemakers are influenced by 50 Hz magnetic fields.

Recently several investigations have been published which report threshold values for biological effects in the order of the exposure limits or at even lower values (section 4.2). Examples are the development of mammary tumours in animals treated by chemical initiators and exposed to a 50 Hz magnetic field of 100 µT (Löscher *et al* 1993), the enhancement of a chemical promoter (TPA)-induced inhibition of transformed cell growth by a 100 µT field (Cain *et al* 1993), or observations that the outgrowth of neurites *in vitro* is adversely affected by magnetic fields of 10 to 20 µT and above (Blackman *et al* 1993a and 1993b). At present these data are insufficient to make a health risk assessment. More studies are necessary to establish whether these effects exist.

However, in view of such studies and the problem of electromagnetic interference with pacemakers and other implants and uncertainties concerning possible long-term effects, in a few countries (for example, Sweden (SSI 1993), Switzerland (BUWAL 1993), Germany (SSK 1995)) aspects of prevention concerning public health, are being considered. In these countries, the principle of precaution is considered by decision makers especially when new technologies are developed using electrical energy or when sources of electromagnetic fields are built near public dwellings. The concept termed "prudent avoidance" (Morgan *et al* 1989) has been suggested as an intermediate approach for decision makers in the face of present uncertainties about electromagnetic fields and possible health risks. It derives from socioeconomic and political considerations and it has no established scientific basis. It has not been generally accepted.

Some epidemiological reports present data indicative of an increase in the incidence of cancer among children, adults, and occupational groups. The studies suggest an association with exposure to weak 50 or 60 Hz magnetic fields. These associations cannot be satisfactorily explained by current knowledge about the interaction of 50/60 Hz electromagnetic fields with living systems. Some epidemiological studies suggest an increased cancer incidence at values of magnetic flux density of about 0.25 μT. This magnetic flux density would induce a current density that is well below those levels normally occurring in the body. The epidemiological studies have been reviewed and evaluated by several national and international radiation protection bodies. The final conclusions of different expert groups are quite similar: although the more recent data reflect some improvements in methodology in laboratory studies and in epidemiological studies, the data related to cancer do not establish that electromagnetic fields cause cancer. The data do not provide a basis for health risk assessment of human exposure to power frequency fields.

6.3 Electromagnetic fields and radiation of frequencies between 100 kHz and 300 GHz

Two categories of effects are sufficiently well understood to be considered for health hazard assessment, ie, the evidence that absorption of radiofrequency energy causes tissue heating and that at frequencies below about 100 MHz currents can be induced in humans by physical contact with ungrounded metallic objects.

Many of the biological effects of acute exposure to radiofrequency and microwave radiation are consistent with responses to induced heating, resulting either in frank rises in tissue or body temperature of about 1°C or more, or in responses for minimising the total heat load. Most responses have been reported at SARs above about 1 to 2 W kg^{-1} in different animal species (particularly primate) exposed under various environmental conditions. These data indicate the sort of responses that are likely to occur in humans subjected to a sufficient heat load.

Healthy subjects at rest in light clothing and in ambient conditions of around 21 to 22°C and relative humidity of around 50% with adequate ventilation seem able to dissipate radiofrequency power at SARs of 1 W kg^{-1}, and to up to 4 W kg^{-1} for short periods. Sweating and an increase in breathing and heart rate have been seen in volunteers in response to whole-body SARs in the upper part of this range after exposure for about 20 minutes. It is likely that adverse environmental conditions, such as high temperature or humidity, and moderate physical exercise will restrict this range of tolerable SAR. This may also be the case for people under medication or with conditions which impair thermoregulation. Conversely, heat tolerant or acclimatised people in low environmental temperatures may accommodate higher SARs.

Typical deliberate emitters include radiobroadcasting and television stations, radar installations, and electronic wireless communications systems. These sources can be classified in different ways and classifications may vary from country to country depending on attitudes toward possible environmental and health effects. Broadcasting stations are significant sources of RF exposure, and in view of the ever increasing popularity of mobile (portable and mounted on vehicles) transmitters for personal use, field intensities in the close vicinity of antennae of these transmitters may be of concern in some countries from the point of view of population exposure.

Medical microwave and RF equipment (mostly medical diathermy) is a particular class of deliberate emitters designed and used for the irradiation of human subjects to obtain beneficial effects. In this case, the intended human exposure is carried out under professional supervision and constitutes part of a medical practice. The contribution of medical uses to the general population exposure is difficult to evaluate and varies from country to country. Although individual patients may absorb large quantities of energy, the exposure is limited to selected body areas and limited in time. However, medical microwave and RF equipment is also a source of unintentional radiation because during irradiation sessions considerable scattering of electromagnetic fields may occur. The unintentional exposure of both patient and personnel usually involves the whole body.

The magnitude of SARs associated with the exposures to which the public are likely to be subject to are given in table 6.1 (Allen 1991).

TABLE 6.1 Estimated whole body averaged SAR for specific exposure situations (Allen 1991)*

Source/exposure locations	SAR (W kg^{-1})
300 m from the base of a 1000 kW ERP UHF TV transmitter	<0.001
70 to 80 m from centre of 100 W HF array	0.04
0.5 to 1 km from a 100 kW HF vertically polarised transmitter	<0.001
50 cm from a car mounted 27 MHz, 4 W CB antenna	0.05
550 m in the beam of a 1.3 GHz stationary air-traffic control radar	0.04
5 m from a 10 GHz, 100 mW traffic control radar	<0.001
30 cm from a microwave oven with maximum permitted leakage	0.04
12 m from 10 GHz 300 W, tracking radar	6.10
100 m from tracking radar	0.04

*These examples are related to measurements made at specific locations and caution should be exercised in regarding the examples as typical of a source type.

When a person touches a metallic object such as a car, van, or bus situated in an RF field, large currents may flow through the body that are considerably in excess of those that would cause perception, pain, and even burns in some cases. However, these effects depend on the current density in tissue, rather than on the current value. It has been noted that burns will occur when current densities in the skin exceed 3 to 4 kA m^{-2}.

Among the various, possible effects of interference induced by radiofrequency and microwave radiation, the effects of cellular phones on pacemaker patients play an outstanding role. Recently, studies conducted in Italy and in Switzerland (Eicher *et al* 1994) show that cardiac pacemakers implanted in patients can be affected by electromagnetic field from cellular telephones.

The Italian study was conducted with 2 analogue and 2 digital cellular phone models. The digital models were 2 W maximum power, working with the new European standard GSM; the analogue ones were 0.6 W maximum power and worked with the TACS standard. Both standards operate in the 900 MHz range. The electromagnetic fields radiated by the phones interfered with 15 out of 27 and 10 out of 25 pacemakers tested *in vitro* with the GSM and the TACS signal, respectively; GSM interference was detected also in 26 out of 101 pacemaker patients. Specifically, pulse inhibition, asynchronous pacing, synchronisation, undersensing and oversensing effects were detected. The effect, however, was observed only when the phone antenna was positioned directly over the pacemaker head, up to a distance of 13 cm *in vitro* and 10 cm *in vivo*. Once the phone was removed, in no case was there permanent malfunctioning or reprogramming of the pacemakers. The results indicate that pacemaker patients may be in a potentially hazardous situation if they carry a cellular phone in close proximity to the implant, for instance in the inner pocket of a jacket (Barbaro *et al* 1994 and 1995).

There are other areas of biological investigation in which effects have been described which have health implications but which are not sufficiently well established or delineated to provide a basis for restricting human exposure. In particular, the possibility that exposure to radiofrequency or microwave radiation might influence the process of carcinogenesis is of particular concern.

6.4   Visible and infrared radiation

The main source of visible and IRR with respect to public exposure is the sun. Other sources for which published data exist for health hazard assessment include lighting systems. Insufficient published information for health hazard assessment exists for other sources. In the following health hazard assessment, the exposure guidelines promulgated by the American Conference of Governmental Industrial Hygienists have been used (ACGIH 1992).

6.4.1   Solar radiation

The published data relating to solar radiation measured at the Earth's surface are often given for combined incident radiation for visible radiation and IRR. The total solar irradiance at the Earth's surface varies from 500 to 1100 W m^{-2} (Sliney and Wolbarsht 1980). The mean direct irradiance can be about 90 W m^{-2} for certain exposure scenarios, with direct retinal burn and blue-light weighted irradiances of about 120 and 8 W m^{-2} (effective). However, in most cases, there are no perceived hazards from direct solar visible and IR, because the natural aversion responses of the eye are respected by the majority of people, and fixation is unlikely, because direct viewing of the sun is uncomfortable to the eye. In addition the eyes are afforded some protection, from direct exposure, by the anatomical structure of the head with the eyebrow and eyelids providing some shielding.

The diffuse solar radiation component does not have the same distribution as the direct component (which approximates to a black body at 6000 K) and the radiance is very much lower (by a factor of approximately 5 10^{-5}), due to the much larger solid angle than for the direct radiation (Sliney and Wolbarsht 1980). The direct infrared irradiance is 40 W m^{-2}, which is 40% of the ACGIH limit (100 W m^{-2}) intended to protect the lens.

6.4.2   Emissions from other sources

Published data from non-solar sources are limited. The ambient radiant exitance of surrounding structures and the ground may vary from 10 to 400 W m^{-2} (Sliney and Wolbarsht, 1980). As regards room lighting, published blue-light radiance values for low pressure fluorescent lamps are in the range 1 to 10 W m^{-2} sr^{-1} , which is only 1 to 10% of the limit (100 W m^{-2} sr^{-1}) (Sliney and Wolbarsht 1980). In some cases, staring at desk-top lamps and uplighters for times greater than about a minute could result in the exposure limit for the retinal blue-light hazard being exceeded (McKinlay *et al* 1989). The measured blue-light radiance value for a high pressure sodium fluorescent lamp (150 W), used for example in street lighting, is 850 W m^{-2} sr^{-1}, which is

8.5 times the limit (100 W m^{-2} sr^{-1}) (Sliney and Wolbarsht 1980). The time to exceed the limit (10^6 J m^{-2} sr^{-1}) is about 20 minutes.

6.5 Ultraviolet radiation

The main source of UVR with respect to public exposure is the sun. Other sources for which published data exist for health hazard assessment include lighting systems (in the home and public places), medical sources (in hospitals and dentists surgeries) and welding arcs. A summary of information on these sources is provided in table 6.2.

TABLE 6.2 Effective irradiances and times to reach exposure limits or 1 MED (250 J m^{-2} (effective)) (McKinlay and Diffey 1987 (CIE), IRPA 1991, ACGIH 1992)

Source	Organ	Weighting function	Time to exceed limit or 1 MED (Measurement distance)
Sun (average)	Eye	IRPA/UVA	17 min
Sun (average)	Eye	IRPA/actinic	108 min
Sun (average)	Skin	IRPA/actinic	78 min
Sun (average)	Skin	CIE/erythema	154 min
Sun (maximum)	Eye	IRPA/UVA	390 s
Sun (maximum)	Eye	IRPA/actinic	25 min
Sun (maximum)	Skin	IRPA/actinic	16 min
Sun (maximum)	Skin	CIE/erythema	32 min
Domestic lighting (fluorescent)	Eye and skin	ACGIH	> 8 h (1.35 m)
Domestic lighting (fluorescent)	Skin	CIE/erythema	10–15 days
Solarium lamps	Eye and skin	ACGIH	3–8 h (1.35 m)
Solarium lamps	Skin	CIE/erythema	7–115 h
Industrial low pressure discharge	Eye and skin	ACGIH	5–8 min
Industrial low pressure discharge	Skin	CIE/erythema	23–35 min
Miniature fluorescent lamps	Eye and skin	ACGIH	> 8 h (0.65 m)
Miniature fluorescent lamps	Skin	CIE/erythema	> 8 h (0.65 m)
Desk top lamps (tungsten halogen)	Eye and skin	ACGIH	14 min–8 h (0.3 m)
Desk top lamps (tungsten halogen)	Skin	CIE/erythema	74 min–58 h
Medical sources	Eye	ACGIH/UVA	40–100 s
Medical sources	Skin	ACGIH/actinic	1 s–4 h
Welding arcs	Eye and skin	ACGIH/actinic	8 s–2 min

6.5.1 Solar radiation

The solar UVR exposure received by an individual depends on three factors:

• the ambient solar UVR.

- the fraction of ambient exposure received on appropriate anatomical sites.
- the exposure habits outdoors.

Estimates of personal exposure to solar UVR for an indoor worker in the UK have been obtained by direct measurement and by modelling (Slaper and van der Leun 1987, Rosenthal *et al* 1991, Diffey 1992). The results indicate that around 100 MED per year is received, mainly to hands, forearms and face. This is approximately 5% of the total ambient and comprises about 40 MED from weekend exposure and the remainder from vacational exposure and pursuits such as outdoor lunch breaks and daily travelling. For children, the annual personal exposure is estimated as about 150 MED, since there is a greater opportunity for outdoor exposure. This annual exposure comprises about 90 MED from recreational exposure (out of school) and about 30 MED from both vacational exposure and exposures associated with school playtime and lunch time. However, there will be large variations in the annual personal exposures within a given population group depending upon the propensity for outdoor activities. UV-exposure assessment of the eyes is particularly complex, due to among other factors, the strong dependence on ocular exposure on geometrical factors, figure 6.1 (Sliney 1994).

6.5.2 Lighting systems

Fluorescent lamps The most commonly used in the domestic environment are white, cool white and warm white. Measured UV irradiances on a range of fluorescent lamps at 1.35 m (Whillock *et al* 1988) have been weighted, according to ACGIH recommendations (ACGIH 1986). The weighted irradiances have all been normalised for an associated illuminance of 500 lux and are below the recommended maximum irradiance for continuous exposure for 8 h of 1 mW m^{-2} (effective) (ACGIH 1986).

Similar results were found for specialist fluorescent lamps used in display and commercial areas (Whillock *et al* 1988). These values are all for bare tubes whereas in practice most luminaires have some kind of attenuation in the form of an optical diffuser which further reduces the UV irradiance. The biological weighting of results from measurements on miniature (compact) fluorescent lamps at 0.65 m indicate that they do not constitute a significant UV hazard (Whillock *et al* 1990).

A selection of fluorescent lamps used in sunbed systems have also been measured at 1.35 m (Whillock *et al* 1988). The data are for single lamps so that scaling is required to assess actual levels encountered by users of solaria etc. The ACGIH weighted values ranged from 0.1 to 3.0 (effective), allowing exposure times of 3 to 90 h.

Tungsten halogen lamps Measurements have been made on a range of tungsten halogen lamps (McKinlay *et al* 1989). The ACGIH weighting (ACGIH 1988) gave effective irradiances ranging from 0.7 to 35 mW m^{-2} (effective) allowing exposure times ranging from about 15 min to 12 h before recommended limits are exceeded.

6.5.3 Medical sources

Measurements have been made on optical sources used in clinical areas such as physiotherapy, paediatrics, dermatology, and dentistry and in hospital kitchens (electronic fly killer) (Diffey and Langley 1986). Only sources used for clinical purposes were found in some circumstances to exceed exposure criteria, but these were used under clinical supervision.

6.5.4 Welding

Exposure of the public could result from the use of welding arcs in public areas. The UVR emitted by arc welding systems is dependent upon the arc current, arc length, nature of the gas and the metals forming the weld. Measurement data on three commonly used processes, TIG (tungsten inert gas), PAW (plasma arc welding) and MMA (manual metal arc) have been published (Bennett and Harlen 1980). The actinic (200–315 nm) effective irradiances were measured in the range from 0.5 to 4 W m^{-2} (effective) using ACGIH weighting values from 200 to 315 nm (ACGIH 1980). These irradiances were measured at a distance of 1 m from the arc. Exposure to these levels would result in doses (radiant exposures) in excess of the limit 30 J m^{-2} (effective) within a time range of about 10 s to 2 min.

6.6 Laser radiation

Lasers are encountered in many areas where public exposure is possible, although in most instances the probability of incurring injury is low. This is due either to the low output power or the design of the laser system limiting the degree of exposure.

The following uses have been identified relating to possible public exposure to lasers.

- Display and entertainment purposes.
- Medical - surgery and physiotherapy.
- The `beauty' industry.
- Compact disc (CD) players.
- Bar code readers, eg (fixed and hand-held) at cash desks in supermarkets and shops.
- Other (usually associated with occupational) uses; eg, surveying and distance measurement, metal cutting and welding, pointers in lecture theatres, research laboratories, printing, and in communications systems (eg, telephone networks) in conjunction with fibre optic highways.

6.6.1 Lasers used for display and entertainment purposes

The type and power of the laser used for display or entertainment purposes will depend on its function. In schools and colleges, it is recommended that only Class 1 or Class 2 lasers are used (IEC, 1993). In practice almost all are Class 2 He-Ne lasers. It is also recommended (IEC 1993) that all lasers used for demonstration, display and entertainment purposes in unsupervised areas are Class 1 or Class 2 and that higher power laser should only be used when under the control of an experienced, well-trained operator and/or when spectators are prevented from exposure to levels exceeding the maximum permissible exposure (MPE).

Class 1 lasers are either intrinsically safe or safe by design. It follows therefore that the MPE for eye and skin will not be exceeded when using these lasers. For Class 2 lasers (visible) it is assumed that the blink reflex will prevent the exposure to the eye from exceeding the MPE. Calculations show that for a CW He-Ne laser, output power 1 mW and beam diameter 7 mm, the skin MPE will not be exceeded.

Lasers most commonly found in discos, at rock concerts or in stage shows are generally high power devices. Outdoor laser displays normally require high output Class 4 (between 2 and 60 W) devices in order to create the required optical effects. The most commonly used laser for this purpose is the CW argon ion laser with its main emission lines at 514.5 nm (green) and 488 nm (blue). It is not unusual to find the main beam has a power of between 2 and 60 W. Direct exposure may be hazardous.

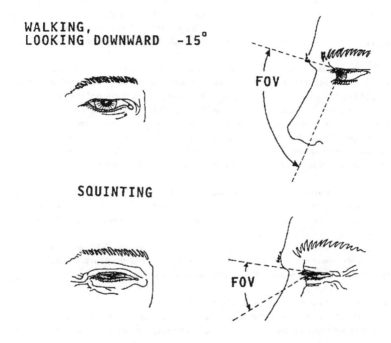

FIGURE 6.1 Geometrical factors affect ocular exposure to UVR. The effect of squinting is to reduce field-of-view (FOV) and strongly limit ocular exposure to UVR from sky scatter. The upper lid blocks most of the skylight and generally covers the upper limbus. (courtesy of Sliney 1994).

6.6.2 Medical lasers

Lasers are used as a tool for surgical processes and physiotherapy, as well as in other areas such as in acupuncture (in place of needles). Therefore, members of the public are likely to be exposed to laser radiation by this means, although quantifying the exposure is impossible as each person carrying out the process will make a clinical judgement for the particular patient. In surgery commonly used lasers (Class 4) are CO_2, YAG and ruby lasers. For ophthalmic surgery a commonly used laser is a Class 4 argon ion laser. In physiotherapy lasers are being used as a source of `deep' heat. Typical lasers used for this are near IRR diode lasers or Class 3B He-Ne lasers with a CW output of 50 mW. The beam is normally delivered via a probe with a lens at the end.

Medical lasers are widely used in clinical areas such as cardiovascular and chest surgery, dermatology, neurosurgery, and ophthalmology. They have also found applications in dental surgery (CO_2, 10.6 μm) (Carruth and McKenzie 1986). The output power of lasers used in the medical area can range from 3 W (diode-800 nm) to 100 W (CO_2, 10.6 μm, beam diameter = 8 mm, and Nd:YAG, 1.064 μm, beam diameter = 400 μm) for continuous wave emitting systems. Pulsed lasers can emit powers of 20 W (Tm:YAG, 2.01 μm-beam diameter = 400 μm and Ho:YAG, 2.14 μm-beam diameter = 400 μm) to 100 W (CO_2, 10.6 μm-beam diameter = 150 μm) (Sliney and Trokel 1993). He-Ne CW lasers are used for acupuncture but no data on exposure levels are available.

6.6.3 Lasers used in the `beauty' industry

Lasers are used in the `beauty' industry, for example, it is claimed to reduce wrinkles and rejuvenate skin. Quantifying the amount of radiation to which the client is exposed is impossible as it will vary from operator to operator.

Lasers used to rejuvenate skin and lessen wrinkles are usually He-Ne or GaAs. Reports vary as to the power output and class of these lasers and no information is available as to typical exposure times although between 12 and 20 treatments seem to be normal.

6.6.4 Lasers used in compact disc (CD) players

CD players are Class 1 laser products and are totally enclosed so that exposure is only a possibility upon removal of the casing. No member of the public should be exposed above the MPE provided the unit is not dismantled.

6.6.5 Lasers used in bar code readers

Lasers used for reading bar codes should be installed such that no member of the public exceeds the MPE. Most bar code readers are either Class 1 (inherently safe by virtue of the engineering design) or Class 2 (limit 1 mW) and should therefore not present a hazard provided the aversion responses are respected.

6.6.6 Lasers used in other areas

The use of lasers to produce carrier beams for communication has increased rapidly in recent years and it is expected that this will continue. This is of particular interest since laser/fibre optic outputs will be introduced into the home environment, but as yet there are no published data on possible emissions.

Laser pointers, such as those used in lecture theatres, etc, are normally Class 2 He-Ne lasers or Class 3b laser diodes and therefore staring at the direct laser beam should be avoided.

6.7 Summary

6.7.1 Static and slowly time varying fields

Static electric fields act on the surface of the body. This may be accompanied by hair movement and other sensory stimulation in fields greater than 10 kV m^{-1} becoming annoying at field strengths greater than 25 kV m^{-1}.

Static electric fields induce surface charges on conducting objects. Currents may pass through grounded persons in contact with such objects. Field strengths greater than approximately 5–7 kV m^{-1} produce a wide variety of hazards associated with spark discharges and contact currents from underground conductors within the field.

Concerning static magnetic fields, current scientific knowledge does not suggest any detrimental effect on major development, behavioural and physiological parameters for transient exposures to fields up to 2 T. From the established mechanisms of interaction, long-term exposure to static magnetic fields up to 200 mT should not have adverse consequences on health.

However, indirect field coupling may be more important than direct field coupling. For people with cardiac pacemakers, ferromagnetic implants, and implanted electronic devices, there are health risks if the magnetic flux density exceeds several mT. The majority of cardiac pacemakers are unlikely to be affected in fields less than 0.5 mT. There are also other electronic aids in use that may be susceptible to static magnetic flux densities above a few mT particularly if the person is moving within the field.

6.7.2 Time varying electromagnetic fields of frequencies less than 100 kHz

For time varying electric fields, indirect field coupling may be more important than direct field coupling. For direct field coupling, 90% of exposed persons have detection threshold of about 10 to 15 kV m^{-1} due to sensations from hair vibration or tingling between body and clothes. Although these effects are not considered to be a hazard, they can become an annoyance.

Thresholds for perception or pain due to contact currents or spark discharges are relatively low and are dependent on the frequency and field strength, the size of the object and on the person's impedance to ground.

Examples are 2 to 2.5 kV m^{-1} for the median touch perception for children, finger contact with a car and 8 to 10 kV m^{-1} for a painful shock for children, finger contact with a truck. The threshold for the perception of spark discharges by 10% of a group of volunteers close to an earthed object has been reported to be 0.6 to 1.5 kV m^{-1} at 50/60 Hz, with a similarly defined threshold for annoyance of 2 to 3.5 kV m^{-1}.

Health risk assessment for time varying magnetic fields is based on induced electric fields and currents in the body. From current scientific knowledge it may be concluded that functions of the central nervous system may be adversely affected by current densities only above 10 mA m^{-2} between 10 Hz and 1 kHz and by progressively larger current densities at frequencies above and below this frequency range.

Several laboratory studies have been conducted on people exposed to 50/60 Hz magnetic fields. None of these investigations has revealed adverse clinical or significant physiological changes. The strongest magnetic flux density used was a 5 mT, 50 Hz field to which subjects were exposed for 4 h.

The lowest sensitivity thresholds for magnetophosphenes are about 2 mT at 20 Hz and about 5 mT at 50 Hz.

The threshold value for a malfunction of some sensitive unipolar cardiac pacemakers is 20 µT (50 Hz) under worst case conditions. At about 200 µT most of the implanted pacemakers are influenced by magnetic 50 Hz fields.

Some epidemiological reports present data indicative of an increase in the incidence of cancer among children, adults, and occupational groups. These association cannot be satisfactorily explained by the available theoretical basis for the interaction of 50/60 Hz electromagnetic fields with living systems. The epidemiological studies have been reviewed and evaluated by several national and international radiation protection bodies. The final conclusions of different expert groups are quite similar: although the more recent data reflect some improvements in methodology in laboratory studies and in epidemiological studies, the data related to cancer do not provide a basis for health risk assessment on human exposure to power frequency magnetic fields.

6.7.3 Electromagnetic fields and radiation of frequencies between 100 kHz and 300 GHz

Several factors need to be assessed in the health assessment of exposure to radiofrequency radiation including: heating caused by the absorption of RF energy, the induction of currents in people by physical contact with ungrounded metallic objects, the absorption of RF energy in the form of pulsed fields. Here the great power densities in the pulse should be considered separately from the average. Auditory perception is an example of a pulsed RF field effect.

Limited experimental evidence and theoretical calculations suggest that exposure of resting people in moderate environmental conditions at whole body SARs in the range 1 to 4 W kg^{-1} for 30 minutes results in body temperature increases of less than 1°C. In addition, a review of the animal data indicates a threshold for behaviour responses in the same 1 to 4 W kg^{-1} range.

Higher energy absorption rates in extremities and limited body regions do not appear to cause adverse effects, for SAR values below thresholds that are dependent on the body part and the volume.

For some people, for example taking certain drugs, thermoregulatory capacity may be reduced and as a result tolerance for the combined effects of RF exposure, exercise, solar radiation, and high ambient temperature, may be lower.

Superficial and deep burns may occur as a result of contact with metallic objects exposed to RF fields over a wide frequency range. Sufficiently high current densities for contact burns can be attained in RF fields that are too low to cause direct heating or stimulation. Thresholds depend on the size and shape of the object, field frequency, length and type of contact, and other parameters.

At frequencies below approximately 1 MHz, interactions of RF fields with biological systems and potential hazards can be considered in terms of induced currents and current densities.

The use of induced current densities is only appropriate for the assessment of acute, immediate effects. The wave form of the RF field is an important factor to be considered in the response of biological systems.

Experimental data suggest that thresholds for the biological effects of absorbed energy at frequencies above hundreds of MHz, when in the form of short duration pulses (a few tens of μs), are lower than those for continuous fields at the same average energy level and the same SAR. This indicates that the peak value of energy transfer to the biological object can be an important determinant of the biological effect. A well-investigated effect is the perception of pulsed fields, such as from radar, as an audible sound described as a click, chirp, or knocking sensation.

There have been isolated reports that, in certain cell lines and in intact animals, RF exposure has been associated with increased growth rates of cells and tumours and with increases in the incidence of neoplastic transformations. Very few epidemiological studies have been reported. The available evidence does not confirm that RF exposure results in the induction of cancer, or causes existing cancers to progress more rapidly. Because of incompleteness and inconsistencies, the available scientific evidence on carcinogenesis is an inadequate basis for recommendations of health protection guidelines.

6.7.4 Optical radiation

Data on visible and IRR emissions for hazard analysis are limited.

With respect to the blue-light retinal hazard, assessments indicate that under normal usage there is no hazard associated with domestic room and street lighting. The potential hazard exists from viewing the sun directly, particularly with optical aids and from close or prolonged viewing of certain tungsten halogen lighting systems, although the luminances are sufficiently high that comfortable viewing of such sources for prolonged periods is unlikely and the aversion responses of the eye would be activated.

The main source of UVR with respect to public exposure is the sun and individual habits with respect to solar UVR exposure are important in assessing personal risk. Other sources for which published data exist for health hazard assessment are limited but include lighting systems (in the home and public places), medical sources (in hospitals and dentists surgeries) and welding arcs.

Data on emissions from laser sources for hazard analysis are generally more substantial than those for non-laser sources. With lasers being increasingly used in many public areas, such as entertainment and display, hazardous exposure of the general public is possible.

References

ACGIH. 1980. *Threshold limit values and biological exposure indices 1980–81*. Cincinnati, American Conference of Governmental Industrial Hygienists.

ACGIH. 1986. *Threshold limit values and biological exposure indices 1986–87*. Cincinnati, American Conference of Governmental Industrial Hygienists.

ACGIH. 1988. *Threshold limit values and biological exposure indices 1988–89*. Cincinnati, American Conference of Governmental Industrial Hygienists.

ACGIH. 1992. *Threshold limit values and biological exposure indices 1992–93*. Cincinnati, American Conference of Governmental Industrial Hygienists.

Allen, S G. 1991. Radiofrequency field measurements and hazard assessments. J. Radiol. Prot. 11, No. 1, 49–62.

Barbaro, V, Bartolini, P, Donato. A, Militello, C. 1994. GSM Cellular phones interference with implantable pacemakers: *in vitro* observations. *Proceedings of the V International Symposium on Biomedical Engineering*, Santiago de Compostela, September 1994, 275-276.

Barbaro, V, Bartolini, P, Donato, A, Militello, C, Altamura, G, Ammirati, E, Santini, M. 1995. Do European GSM mobile cellular phones pose a potential risk to pacemaker patients? *Pace*, **18**, 1218-1224.

Bennett, A P, and Harlen, F. 1980. Measuring the UV radiation hazard to welders. IN *Welding and Metal Fabrication*, pp 541–549.

Blackman, C F, Benane, S G, House, D E, Pollock, M M. 1993a. Action of 50 Hz magnetic fields on neurite outgrowth in pheochromecytoma cells. *Bioelectromagnetics*, **14**, 273–286.

Blackman, C F, Benane, S G, House, D E. 1993b. Evidence for direct effect of magnetic fields on neurite outgrowth. *FASEP J.*, **7**, 801–806.

BUWAL. 1993. Biologische Auswirkungen nichtionisierender elektromagnetischer Strahlung auf den Menschen und seine Umwelt. 2 Teil: Frequenzbereich 0 Hz bis 100 kHz. Bern, Bundesamt für Umwelt, Wald und Landschaft (in German).

Cain, C D, Thomas, D L, and Adey, W R. 1993. 60 Hz magnetic field acts as co-promoter in focus formation of C3H/10T1/2 cells. *Carcinogenesis*, **14**, 955–960.

Carruth, J A S, and McKenzie, A L. 1986. *Medical Lasers – Science and Clinical Practice*. Bristol and Boston, Adam Hilger, pp 228.

Diffey, B L. 1992. Stratospheric ozone depletion and the risk of non-melanoma skin cancer in a British population. *Phys. Med. Biol.* **37**, 2267-2279.

Diffey, B L, and Langley, F C. 1986. Evaluation of ultraviolet radiation hazards in hospitals. York, Institute of Physical Sciences in Medicine, Report No. 49.

Eicher, B, Ryser, H, Knafl, U, Burkart, F, Naegeli, B, Deola, M, Babotai, I, Kuster N. 1994. Effects of TDMA-modulated hand-held telephones on pacemakers. *Abstract Book of the Sixteenth Annual Meeting of the Bioelectromagnetics Society (BEMS)*, Copenhagen.

IEC. 1993. *Radiation safety of laser products, equipment classification, requirements and user's guide.* International Electrotechnical Commission Publication 825, Parts 1 and 2.

IRPA. 1991. *IRPA Guidelines on Protection Against Non-Ionizing Radiation.* The International Radiation Protection Association (Duchêne, A S, Lakey, J R A and Repacholi, M H, eds). Oxford, Pergamon Press.

Löscher, W, Mevissen, M, Lehmacher, W, and Stamm, A. 1993. Tumour promotion in a breast cancer model by exposure to a weak alternating magnetic field. *Cancer Lett.*, **71**, 75–81.

McKinlay, A F, and Diffey, B L. 1987. A reference action spectrum for ultraviolet induced erythema in human skin. *CIE J*, **6**, No. 1., 17–22.

McKinlay, A F, Whillock, M J, and Meulemans, C C E. 1989. UVR and blue-light emissions from spotlights incorporating tungsten halogen lamps. Chilton, NRPB-R228 (London, HMSO).

Morgan, M G, Nair, I, and Florig, H K. 1989. Biological effects of power frequency electric and magnetic fields. Washington DC, Office of Technology Assessment.

Rosenthal, F S, West, S K, Munoz, B, Emmett, E A, Strickland, P T, and Taylor, H R. 1991. Ocular and facial skin exposure to ultraviolet radiation in sunlight: a personal exposure model with application to a worker population. *Health Physics*, **61**, 77-86.

Slaper, H, and van der Leun, J C. 1987. Human Exposure to Ultraviolet Radiation: Quantitative Modelling of Skin Cancer Incidence. *Human Exposure to Ultraviolet Radiation - Risks and Regulations*. International Congress Series 744. (Passchier, W F, and Bosnjakovic, B F M, eds). Amsterdam, Excerpta Medica.

Sliney, D, and Wolbarsht, M. 1980. *Safety with Lasers and Other Optical Sources.* New York and London, Plenum Press.

Sliney, D H, and Trokel, S L. 1993. *Medical Lasers and Their Safe Use*. New York and London, Springer-Verlag, p 145.

Sliney, D H. 1994. Epidemiological studies of sunlight and cataract: the critical factor of ultraviolet exposure geometry. Ophthalmic Epidemiology $\underline{1}$(2), 107–109.

SSI. 1993. Swedish Radiation Protection Institute: SSI-Policy: Health risks from electromagnetic fields. Stockholm, SSI-News No. 2, February 1993.

SSK. 1995. German Radiation Protection Commission: Protection against electric and magnetic fields of the distribution and application of electric energy (in German). Recommendation approved 16/17 February 1995, in press.

UNEP/WHO/IRPA. 1984. *Extremely Low Frequency (ELF) Fields, Environmental Health Criteria 35*. Geneva, World Health Organization.

UNEP/WHO/IRPA. 1987. *Magnetic Fields, Environmental Health Criteria 69*. Geneva, World Health Organization.

Whillock, M J, Clark, I E, McKinlay, A F, Todd, C D, and Mundy, S J. 1988. Ultraviolet radiation levels associated with the use of fluorescent general lighting, UV-A and UV-B lamps in the workplace and home. Chilton, NRPB-R221 (London, HMSO).

Whillock, M J, McKinlay, A F, Kemmlert, J, and Forsgren, P G. 1990. Ultraviolet radiation emissions from miniature (compact) fluorescent lamps. Lighting Res. Technol., **22**, No. 3, 125–128.

7 International and European Union Member States guidelines and regulations for protection against NIR

7.1 International

The following provides a brief review of international recommended limits and the basic underlying rationale.

In assessing health risks, the terms "effect" and "damage" are often confused. Whenever there is an interaction between radiation and living matter, there is always an effect which can either be without any biological consequences or can involve favourable or damaging consequences to health. The International Radiation Protection Association/International Non-Ionizing Radiation Committee (IRPA/INIRC) and its successor body the International Commission on Non-Ionizing Radiation Protection (ICNIRP) have established a protection doctrine based on the principles that compliance with health protection standards ensures adequate protection and that this compliance should be guaranteed by performance standards for devices, or if not possible, by the application of appropriate operational protection measures. The limit values should not be considered as a precise boundary between risk and no risk. For electromagnetic fields the ICNIRP rationale is that separate limits may be set for occupational exposure that differ from those for the general population, because occupational exposure in principle concerns only adults, limited to the working time and is subject to control. In addition workers may benefit from medical surveillance and should be aware of the hazards and trained in protective measures. Performance standards for all categories of apparatus should in particular ensure safety requirements and a minimisation of the emission. The IRPA/INIRC and ICNIRP recommendations are intended as guidelines for national authorities who are responsible for the elaboration and implementation of regulations.

The European Commission has drawn up a proposal for a Council of the European Union Directive on the minimum health and safety requirements regarding the exposure of workers to the risks arising from physical agents (CEU 1994). The physical agents to which the Directive applies are noise, mechanical, vibration, optical radiation and fields and waves.

The European Committee for Electrical Standardisation (CENELEC) has produced two pre-standards on human exposure to electromagnetic fields, one providing basic restrictions and field reference levels for low frequency fields, 0 Hz to 10 kHz (CENELEC 1995a), and another covering the frequency range 10 kHz to 300 GHz (CENELEC 1995b). Both standards advise on exposure of the general public as well as workers.

The practical implementation of these pre-standards in the member states of the European Union is uncertain, as concern has been expressed, both at a national level and from the European Commission, about the status of CENELEC in relation to setting standards concerned with human health. Unlike ICNIRP, which is demonstrably independent of industry, the CENELEC committees which formulated these pre-standards comprised, among others, representatives from industry including the electricity supply and telecommunications industries.

The *Ad Hoc* Working Group is of the opinion that technical committees such as those of CENELEC perform excellent work in areas of their technical expertise. By working out measurement methods and detailed technical specifications, these committees provide the necessary background for regulation to be established by the relevant political responsible bodies. However, the work of such technical committees should not include the evaluation of health risks for people from exposure to electromagnetic fields.

7.1.1 Static fields

ICNIRP limits for static magnetic fields are summarised in table 7.1. The basic interaction mechanisms considered are magnetic induction, magnetomechanical effects and electronic interaction. Current scientific knowledge does not suggest any detrimental effect on major developmental, behavioural, and physiological parameters in higher organisms for transient exposure to static magnetic flux densities up to 2 T. The restriction to 200 mT is a conservative one based on the present lack of any knowledge of long-term effects of exposure. Additional considerations of potential hazards due to interference of magnetic fields with electronic devices lead to the recommendation that locations with magnetic flux densities >0.5 mT should be posted with appropriate warning signs. It is difficult to give precise guidance as to the effect of static magnetic fields on implanted ferromagnetic devices or materials. Depending on factors such as gradient of the field, degree of ferromagnetism in the implant, its size, its orientation, some ferromagnetic materials may be moved or dislodged by static fields as low as a few millitesla. Considerations of potential hazards due to movement or dislodgement of implanted ferromagnetic materials or from flying objects, lead to the recommendation that areas with magnetic flux densities >3 mT should be indicated by specific warning signs.

TABLE 7.1 Exposure limits for static magnetic fields* (ICNIRP 1994)

Exposure characteristics	Magnetic flux density
Occupational	
Whole working day (time-weighted average)	200 mT
Ceiling value	2 T
Limbs	5 T
General public	
Continuous exposure	40 mT

*People with cardiac pacemakers and other implanted electrically activated devices, or with ferromagnetic implants, may not be adequately protected by the limits given here. The majority of cardiac pacemakers are unlikely to be affected by exposure to fields below 0.5 mT. People with some ferromagnetic implants or electrically activated devices (other than cardiac pacemakers) may be affected by fields above a few mT. When magnetic flux densities exceed 3 mT, precautions should be taken to prevent hazards from flying metallic objects. Analogue watches, credit cards, magnetic tapes, computer disks, etc, may be adversely affected by exposure to 1 mT but this is not a safety concern for humans. Occasional access of members of the public to special facilities where magnetic flux densities exceed 40 mT can be allowed under controlled conditions provided that the appropriate occupational exposure limit is not exceeded.

7.1.2 50/60 Hz electric and magnetic fields

The limits for power frequency electric and magnetic fields are summarised in table 7.2. The considered coupling mechanisms include the induction of a surface charge on a body exposed to an electric field. Depending on the exposure conditions, size, shape, and position of the exposed body, this may result in a variable and non-uniform distribution of currents inside the body. Magnetic fields also act on people by inducing electric fields and currents inside the body. Electric charges induced in a conducting object may cause current to pass through a person in contact with it. Magnetic fields coupling to a conductor may also cause currents to pass through the body that is in contact with it. Transient discharges can occur when people and metal objects exposed to strong electric fields come into sufficiently close proximity. The threshold field strength for some people to feel spark discharges is about 3 kV m^{-1}. Electric and magnetic fields may interfere with implanted medical devices. The limits were developed primarily on established or predicted immediate health effects produced by currents induced in the body by external electric and magnetic fields.

TABLE 7.2 Exposure limits for 50/60 Hz electric and magnetic fields (IRPA/INIRC 1990)

Exposure characteristics	Electric field strength (kV m^{-1}) (RMS)	Magnetic flux density (mT) (RMS)
Occupational		
Whole working day	10	0.5
Short term	30[a]	5[b]
For limbs	-	25
General public		
Up to 24 h per day[c]	5	0.1
Few hours per day[d]	10	1

Notes

a   The duration of exposure to fields between 10 and 30 kV m^{-1} may be calculated from the formula t ≤ 80/E, where t is the duration in hours per work day and E is the electric field strength in kV m^{-1}.

b   Maximum exposure duration is 2 h per work day.

c   This restriction applies to open spaces in which members of the general public might reasonably be expected to spend a substantial part of the day, such as recreational areas, meeting grounds.

d   These values can be exceeded for a few minutes per day provided precautions are taken to prevent indirect coupling effects.

The basic criterion is to limit current densities induced in the head and trunk by continuous exposure to electric and magnetic fields to no more than about 10 mA m^{-2}. Continuous occupational exposure should be limited to 4 mA m^{-2} and that of the general population to 2 mA m^{-2}. In addition animal experiments indicate that exposure to strong low frequency electric fields can alter cellular, physiological and behavioural events. The limit of 5 kV m^{-1} for continuous exposure of the general public provides substantial protection from annoyance caused by steady-state contact currents or transient discharges. Threshold of perception, however, may be lower for some people. Interference of electric fields with implanted cardiac pacemakers have not been reported in fields below 2.5 kV m^{-1}. There are no acute effects observed in volunteers resulting from magnetic field exposure up to 5 mT. Data from long-term exposure, however, are sparse. Interference of magnetic fields with cardiac pacemakers depend on pacemaker model. Assuming worst-case conditions, interference flux densities of 15–60 µT may be calculated.

7.1.3 Electromagnetic fields and radiation of frequencies between 100 kHz and 300 GHz

The IRPA/INIRC limits of exposure to radiofrequency electromagnetic fields are summarised in table 7.3 (Klauenberg *et al* 1995). These apply for continuous and amplitude modulated waves. For pulsed fields, it is suggested that the equivalent plane wave power density as averaged over the pulse width should not exceed 1000 times the power density limit in table 7.3, or the field strength not exceed 32 times the field strength limit in this table. The continuous wave (cw) limits were based primarily on thermal considerations, but the objective of protection against athermal effects was also kept in mind. The limits were derived from basic considerations. For frequencies above 10 MHz, whole-body average SAR was chosen as the relevant quantity. Biological evidence shows that the SAR threshold for behavioural effects is around 4 W kg^{-1}. It seems also important to keep body temperature rise from exposure below approximately 1°C. Therefore a limit for the whole-body SAR of 0.4 W kg^{-1} was considered appropriate for workers. A limit of 0.08 W kg^{-1} was advised for the general public. Exposure limits were modified by considerations of the frequency dependence and the non-uniformity of radiofrequency energy deposition in various parts of the body. Another objective was to reduce the hazards of radiofrequency burns and shocks, by reducing the relevant field strength limits.

TABLE 7.3 General public exposure limits to radiofrequency electromagnetic fields and radiation (IRPA/INIRC 1988)

Frequency f (MHz)	Unperturbed RMS field strength		Equivalent plane wave power density	
	Electric E (V m^{-1})	Magnetic H (A m^{-1})	P_{eq} (W m^{-2})	P_{eq} (mW cm^{-2})
0.1–1	87	0.23/f$^{1/2}$	-	-
>1–10	87/f$^{1/2}$	0.23/f$^{1/2}$	-	-
>10–400	27.5	0.073	2	0.2
>400–2000	1.375 f$^{1/2}$	0.0037 f$^{1/2}$	f/200	f/2000
>2000–300000	61	0,61	10	1

7.1.4 Ultraviolet radiation

The exposure limits (EL) for both general and occupational exposure to UVR incident on the skin or eye, where irradiance values are known and the exposure duration is controlled are as follows (Grandolfo et al 1991).

For the UVA spectral region (315 to 400 nm), the total radiant exposure incident on the unprotected eye should not exceed 1.0 J cm^{-2} (10 kJ m^{-2}) within an 8 hour period and the total 8 hour radiant exposure incident on the unprotected skin should not exceed the values given in table 7.4. Values for the relative spectral effectiveness S_λ, are given up to 400 nm to expand the action spectrum into the UVA for determining the EL for skin exposure. For the actinic UVR spectral region (UVC and UVB from 180 to 315 nm), the radiant exposure incident upon the unprotected skin or eye within an 8-hour period should not exceed the values given in table 7.4. Permissible exposure time in seconds for exposure to actinic UVR incident upon the unprotected skin or eye may be computed by dividing 30 J m^{-2} by the value of E_{eff} in W m^{-2}.

TABLE 7.4 UVR exposure limits and spectral weighting function. (IRPA/INIRC 1989)

Wavelength[a] (nm)	Exposure limits (J m^{-2})	Relative spectral effectiveness S_λ
180	2 500	0.012
190	1 600	0.019
200	1 000	0.03
205	590	0.051
210	400	0.075
215	320	0.095
220	250	0.120
225	200	0.150
230	160	0.190
235	130	0.240
240	100	0.300
245	83	0.360
250	70	0.430
254[b]	60	0.500
255	58	0.520
260	46	0.620
265	37	0.810
270	30	1.000
275	31	0.960
280	34	0.880
285	39	0.770
290	47	0.640
295	56	0.540
297[b]	65	0.460
300	100	0.300
303[b]	250	0.190
305	500	0.060
308[b]	1 200	0.026
310	2 000	0.015
313[b]	5 000	0.006
315	$1.0 \cdot 10^4$	0.003

TABLE 7.4 continued

Wavelength[a] (nm)	Exposure limits (J m^{-2})	Relative spectral effectiveness S_λ
316	$1.3\ 10^4$	0.0024
317	$1.5\ 10^4$	0.0020
318	$1.9\ 10^4$	0.0016
319	$2.5\ 10^4$	0.0012
320	$2.9\ 10^4$	0.0010
322	$4.5\ 10^4$	0.00067
323	$5.6\ 10^4$	0.00054
325	$6.0\ 10^4$	0.00050
328	$6.8\ 10^4$	0.00044
330	$7.3\ 10^4$	0.00041
333	$8.1\ 10^4$	0.00037
335	$8.8\ 10^4$	0.00034
340	$1.1\ 10^5$	0.00028
345	$1.3\ 10^5$	0.00024
350	$1.5\ 10^5$	0.00020
355	$1.9\ 10^5$	0.00016
360	$2.3\ 10^5$	0.00013
365	$2.7\ 10^5$	0.00011
370	$3.2\ 10^5$	0.000093
375	$3.9\ 10^5$	0.000077
380	$4.7\ 10^5$	0.000064
385	$5.7\ 10^5$	0.000053
390	$6.8\ 10^5$	0.000044
395	$8.3\ 10^5$	0.000036
400	$1.0\ 10^6$	0.000030

a Wavelengths chosen are representative; other values should be interpolated at
  intermediate wavelengths.
b Emission lines of a mercury discharge spectrum.

These EL values are mainly based on acute adverse health effects such as photokeratitis. They are also intended to limit the risk of chronic effects. They are intended to apply to UVR exposure of the working population, but with some precaution also apply to the general population. However it should be recognised that some rare, highly photosensitive individuals exist who may react adversely to exposure at these levels. Likewise, if individuals are concomitantly exposed to photosensitising agents, a photosensitising reaction can take place. The ELs should be considered absolute limits for the eye, and advisory for the skin because of the wide range of susceptibility to skin injury depending on skin type.

The increasing use of UVR in medicine, in the industrial work environment, for cosmetic use, and partly in consumer products necessitates that greater attention be paid to the potential hazards of this type of electromagnetic radiation. The present understanding of chronic effects and injury mechanisms of UVR is limited, and this problem awaits further research.

7.1.5   Infrared radiation

In the infrared region there are no specific international recommendations for protection from exposure. The most recognised recommendations for the protection of workers in this field are the threshold limit values promulgated by the American Conference of Governmental and Industrial Hygienists (ACGIH 1992). Although these limits are intended only for use in industrial hygiene, and not for use in the evaluation or control of irradiation levels for the general public, they are the only available guidelines for protection from infrared exposure. Values are based on information from industrial experience and from experimental human and animal studies. They are intended to prevent damage to different parts of the eye or the skin mainly from thermal overload due to exposure. They refer to levels to which it is believed that nearly all workers may be repeatedly exposed without adverse health effects. Because of wide variations in individual susceptibility, exposure of a person at, or even below, the limit values may not prevent annoyance, aggravation of a preexisting condition, or physiological damage.

To avoid thermal injury of the cornea and possible delayed effects on the lens of the eye, the infrared radiation exposure should be limited for periods greater than 1000 s to 10 mW cm^{-2}, and for shorter periods to:

$$\sum_{770}^{3000} E_\lambda \ \Delta\lambda \ \leq \ 1.8t^{-3/4} \ W \ cm^{-2} \ (t \leq 10^3 \ s)$$

where E_λ is the spectral irradiance (W cm^{-2}), $\Delta\lambda$ is the wavelength step used in the assessment and t is the exposure time (s).

To protect the retina in exposure conditions where a strong visual stimulus is absent, near infrared radiation as viewed by the eye should be limited to:

$$\sum_{770}^{3000} L_\lambda \ \Delta\lambda \ \leq \ \frac{0.6}{\alpha}$$

where L_λ is the spectral radiance of the source (W cm^{-2} sr^{-1}) and α is the angle subtended at the eye by the source (radians).

7.2   National

7.2.1   Electromagnetic fields and radiation

Only a few European Union countries have any kind of regulation or guidelines to protect against electromagnetic fields.

Extremely low and low frequency fields

In Austria, based on a proposal by the Austrian Electrotechnical Committee, a pre-norm for low frequency electric and magnetic fields exposure was published in 1994 (Austria 1994). It was developed by a committee formed jointly by the Austrian Standards Institute and the Austrian Electrotechnical Association. Its rationale is essentially the same as that adopted by IRPA/INIRC in guidelines for exposure to 50/60 Hz electric and magnetic fields (IRPA/INIRC 1990). Frequency dependent limits are set in such a way as to match those recommended by IRPA/INIRC at 50 Hz. Austrian limits for unlimited exposure of the general public are reported in table 7.5.

TABLE 7.5 Exposure limits for the general public to electric and magnetic fields in the frequency range 0 Hz to 30 kHz in Austria (Austria 1994)

Frequency (Hz)	Electric field strength (kV m^{-1})	Magnetic flux density (mT)
0	14	1.75
>0–4	10	1.25
4–25	10	5.0/f^a
25–250	250/f^a	5.0/f^a
250–910	250/f^a	0.020
815–10000	0.275	0.020
10000–30000	0.275	0.0001 f$^{2.00b}$

a f = frequency in Hz
b f = frequency in kHz

Because of the importance of the power frequency, a different set of limits is established for short-term exposures to 50 Hz fields. In particular, the exposure limits to the electric and magnetic fields are relaxed by a factor of two and five, respectively, in accordance with IRPA/INIRC (1990).

In Belgium, the only existing limits concern electric fields generated by power lines. These were enforced in 1987 and confirmed in 1988. The limits, which are reported in table 7.6, apply to electric lines of any voltage. No limit is set for the magnetic flux density.

TABLE 7.6 Limits for electric fields generated by power lines in Belgium (Belgium 1988)

Area	Electric field strength (kV m^{-1})
Inhabited areas	5
Road crossings	7
Other areas	10

Fields are measured at 1.5 m from the soil or from buildings

In Germany, the responsibility for radiation protection rests with the Ministry of the Environment.

Recently, the German Radiation Protection Commission passed a recommendation for protection from low frequency electric and magnetic fields (SSK 1995). It is applicable to installations for the supply and use of electric energy.

The Commission recommends the application of the limit values suggested by INIRC to restrict exposure of the public to 50 Hz electric and magnetic fields. Below the limits, however, a possible field strength reduction should remain the subject of consideration, especially for new facilities and products. The Commission also recommends some measures for field reduction.

Based on these recommendations, a law is under discussion in Germany setting limits based on the guidelines of IRPA/INIRC.

In Italy, a law setting exposure limits to 50 Hz electric and magnetic fields was set in place in 1992. The limits apply to any source, and are identical to those recommended by IRPA/INIRC (table 7.7). However, additional requirements are included for the distance from buildings and recreational areas of power lines whose voltage is 132 kV or above. Minimum distances range from 10 m in the case of 132 kV lines to 28 m in the case of 380 kV lines. The law raised great criticism because of its inconsistency. At the above mentioned distances, field strengths are in fact much lower than the exposure limits that are set by the same standard.

TABLE 7.7 Exposure limits for the general public for 50 Hz electric and magnetic fields in Italy (Italy 1992)

	Electric field strength ($kV\ m^{-1}$)	Magnetic flux density (mT)
Continuous exposure	5	0.1
Short-term exposures (few hours per day)	10	1

In the United Kingdom, comprehensive guidance on restrictions on exposure to electromagnetic fields and radiation was issued by NRPB in 1993 (NRPB 1993). Limits are in the form of basic restrictions on current density. Investigations field levels are also issued in the UK guidance, table 7.8. The latter are defined as values of the relevant physical quantities (electric field strength, magnetic flux density, power density, and contact current) provided for the purpose of comparison with values of measured field quantities for investigating whether compliance with basic restrictions is achieved, for example, tables 7.9 and 7.10.

Radiofrequency and microwave radiation

The few existing standards for high-frequency electromagnetic fields are based on similar rationales, although the derived limits are somewhat different. The basic criterion is the same as that adopted by IRPA/INIRC (1988). The most relevant interaction mechanism that may lead to health effects is assumed to be the absorption of electromagnetic energy in the body. Basic limits are therefore set, which aim at limiting average SAR in the body to less than 0.4 W kg^{-1} in the case of occupational exposure. In the case of the general public, a further protection factor is introduced by ICNIRC so that the basic limit is reduced to 0.08 W kg^{-1}. Since dosimetry studies have shown that energy absorption by the human body is strongly frequency dependent, derived limits have been deduced that vary with frequency, with the lowest limits set in the so-called resonance region, where maximum absorption occurs.

To take thermoregulation into account, all limits are averaged over a period (6 minutes, INIRC). This criterion generally applies also in the lowest sub-range of radiofrequencies (below about 10 MHz), where effects are more related to induced currents than to energy absorption within the body.

Different interaction mechanisms are considered to prevail for frequencies below and above about 100 kHz, so that this frequency can conventionally be considered as the cut off between low and high frequencies.

In Germany, a law is under discussion, setting limits based on the guidelines adopted by IRPA/INIRC.

TABLE 7.8 Basic restrictions for exposure to static and time varying electromagnetic fields of frequency less than 300 GHz in the United Kingdom (NRPB 1993)

Frequency range	Basic restriction	Quantity
0 – 1 Hz	200 mT	Magnetic flux density averaged over 24 h in tissues of the head, neck and trunk
	2 T	Maximum magnetic flux density in tissues of the head, neck and trunk
	5 T	Maximum magnetic flux density in the limbs
	100 mA m^{-2}	Induced current density in tissues of the head, neck and trunk
1 – 10 Hz	100/f mA m^{-2}*	
10 Hz – 1 kHz	10 mA m^{-2}	Induced current density in tissues of the head, neck and trunk
1 kHz – 100 kHz	f/100 mA m^{-2}*	
100 kHz – 10 MHz	f/100 mA m^{-2}*	Current density in the head, neck and trunk
100 kHz – 10 GHz	0.4 W kg^{-1}	SAR averaged over the body and over any 15 minute period
	10 W kg^{-1}	SAR averaged over any 10 g in the head or fetus and over any 6 minute period
	10 W kg^{-1}	SAR averaged over any 100 g in the neck and trunk and over any 6 minute period
	20 W kg^{-1}	SAR averaged over any 100 g in the limbs and over any 6 minute period
10 GHz – 300 GHz	100 W m^{-2}	Power density incident on any part of the body
		Between 10 and 300 GHz this can be averaged over 68/f$^{1.05}$ minutes (f in GHz). Above 20 GHz it can be averaged over any 10 second period

* f = frequency in Hz

153

TABLE 7.9 Investigation levels for electric and magnetic fields in the frequency range 0 to 12 MHz in the United Kingdom (NRPB 1993)

Frequency range	Magnetic field strength (Am^{-1})	Magnetic flux density (µT)
< 0.4 Hz	160 000	200 000
0.4 Hz - 1 kHz	64 000/f (Hz)	80 000/f (Hz)
1 kHz - 535 kHz	64	80
535 kHz - 12 MHz	18/f^2 (MHz)	23/f^2 (MHz)

* f = frequency in Hz

TABLE 7.10 Investigation levels for electric and magnetic fields and electromagnetic radiation in the frequency range 12 MHz to 300 GHz in the United Kingdom (NRPB 1993)

Frequency range	Magnetic field strength (Am^{-1})	Magnetic flux density (µT)	Electric field strength (Vm^{-1})	Power density (Wm^{-2})
12 MHz - 200 MHz	0.13	0.16	50	6.6
200 Mhz - 400 MHz	0.66f	0.79f	250f	165f^2
400 MHz - 800 MHz	0.26	0.31	100	26
800 MHz - 155 GHz	0.33f	0.40f	125f	41f^2
1.55 GHz - 300 GHz	0.52	0.62	194	100

f = frequency in GHz

In Austria, guidelines for exposure to radiofrequency and microwave fields from 30 kHz to 3000 GHz were issued in 1992. Limits for the electric and the magnetic field are reported in table 7.11.

TABLE 7.11 Exposure limits for the general public to radiofrequency and microwave electromagnetic fields in Austria (Austria 1992)

Frequency (MHz)	Electric field strength (V m^{-1})	Magnetic field strength (A m^{-1})
0.03–3	275	3.15601
3–30	824/f	3.15601/f$^{1.11332}$
30–300	27.5	0.072
300–1500	1.59615f$^{0.49907}$	0.00397876f$^{0.50788}$
1500–3000000	61.4	0.16

f = frequency in MHz

7.3 Summary

Only a few countries in the European Union have promulgated standards for the protection of the general public against electromagnetic radiation. Austria, Germany and the United Kingdom have recommendations both for low and high frequency electromagnetic fields. In Italy, a law setting limits for exposure to 50 Hz electric and magnetic fields exists, whereas in Belgium the only existing regulation concerns fields generated by power lines. CENELEC has produced two pre-standards.

In both frequency ranges, the adopted rationale is quite similar within different countries, and with respect to international standards. No general distinction is made in the United Kingdom between workers and members of the general public, only between the exposure of adults and children, different from Austria and Italy. In Germany, on the other hand, exposure limits are set with consideration to the exposure environment rather than to a classification of exposed people. Another relevant difference is that limits are compulsory in some countries and only recommended in others. In the UK, field and contact current investigation levels are set as a practical aid to investigate compliance with limits.

References

ACGIH. 1992. *Threshold limit values for chemical substances and physical agents and biological exposure indices 1992–93.* Cincinnati, American Conference of Governmental Industrial Hygienists.

Austria. 1992. "ÖNORM S1120" Microwave and high frequency fields. Permissible exposure limits for the protection of people in the frequency range 30 kHz to 3000 GHz (In German).

Austria. 1994. "ÖNORM S1119/OVE EMV1119" Low frequency electric and magnetic fields. Permissible limits of exposure for the protection of persons in the frequency range 0 Hz to 30 kHz (In German).

Belgium 1988. Réglement Général sur Installations Electriques: Arrêté Royal 20 Avril 1988 (In French).

CENELEC 1995a. Human exposure to electromagnetic fields. Low frequency (0 Hz to 10 kHz). European Prestandard ENV 50166-1.

CENELEC 1995b. Human exposure to electromagnetic fields. High frequency (10 kHz to 300 GHz). European Prestandard ENV 50166-2.

CEU 1994. Amended proposal for a Council Directive on the minimum health and safety requirements regarding exposure of workers to the risks arising from physical agents - Individual Directive in relation to Article 16 of Directive 89/391/EEC. *Official J. of the European Communities,* **37**, 3–29.

Grandolfo, M, Rindi, A, Sliney, D H. (eds). 1991. *Light, Lasers and Synchrotron Radiation. A Health Risk Assessment.* Plenum Press, New York and London.

ICNIRP. 1994. Guidelines on limits of exposure to static magnetic fields. *Health Phys.,* **66**, 100–106.

Italy. 1992. Limiti massimi di esposizione ai campi elettrico e magnetico generati alla frequenza industriale nominale (50 Hz) negli ambienti abitativi e nell'ambiente esterno. DPCM 23 Aprile 1992 (In Italian).

IRPA/INIRC. 1988. Guidelines on limits of exposure to radiofrequency electromagnetic fields in the frequency range from 100 kHz to 300 GHz. *Health Phys.,* **24**, 115–123.

IRPA/INIRC. 1989. Proposed changes to the IRPA/INIRC 1985 guidelines on limits of exposure to ultraviolet radiation. *Health Phys.*, **49**, 331–340.

IRPA/INIRC. 1990. Interim guidelines on limits of exposure to 50/60 Hz electric and magnetic fields. *Health Phys.*, **58**, 113–122.

Klauenberg, B J, Grandolfo, M, Erwin, D N. (eds). 1995. *Radiofrequency Standards: Biological Effects, Dosimetry, Epidemiology, and Public Health Policy.* Plenum Press, New York and London.

NRPB. 1993. "Board statement on restrictions on human exposure to static and time varying electromagnetic fields and radiation". *Documents of the NRPB*, Vol. 4, No. 5.

8 Conclusions and recommendations

The most significant source of exposure to non-ionising radiation for the general public is the sun and, although the adverse health effects of solar ultraviolet radiation including skin cancer are well established, the increased risks associated with high exposure, for example from sunbathing, although not known in detail, appear to be acceptable to many people. In contrast, there has been increasing public concern expressed about possible but not established risks of exposure to low level electromagnetic fields. Levels of electromagnetic fields and radiation generated by humans are much greater than those found in nature. The rapidly expanding industrial and domestic use of electrical and electronic devices contributes to the levels of these fields. Some people may be exposed to significantly greater levels than others because of their proximity to sources and concern is often heightened in such circumstances. Particular concerns have been expressed about possible adverse effects on health of exposure to electromagnetic fields from domestic electricity supplies and in particular from power lines and from hand-held radiotelephones.

Within the EU, biological research on electromagnetic fields is carried out in a rather fragmentary manner at present. There is a clear need to establish a focused and coordinated programme of work, to identify appropriate studies that should be carried out and to establish agreed experimental protocols and appropriate statistical analysis. There is also a need to communicate information about established risks to the general public. A contribution to this would be simple information leaflets.

8.1 Biological research

8.1.1 Static and slowly time varying electric and magnetic fields

The few experimental studies that have been carried out on the biological effects of static electric fields provide no evidence to support suggestions of adverse effects on human health. There is no direct experimental evidence of any adverse effect on human health from acute exposure to static magnetic fields of up to 2 T. There is less information on the effects of chronic exposure but no long term effects have become apparent.

Recommendations

Further biological research does not appear warranted at this stage. However, consideration should be given to compiling data on possible interference with the function of biomedical implants, including ferromagnetic implants which may experience torque in a strong static magnetic field.

8.1.2 Time varying electromagnetic fields of frequencies less than 100 kHz

It is well established that exposure to electric and magnetic fields results in the induction of electric fields and currents in biological tissues, and may result in a variety of nervous system responses.

Most biological studies suggest that exposure to low frequency electromagnetic fields does not have any significant effect on mammalian development.

There is no persuasive evidence that ELF electromagnetic fields are able to influence any of the accepted stages in carcinogenesis. Effects on initiation are extremely unlikely suggesting that if there is an effect it will be at the level of promotion or progression. Here, the evidence remains confused with no clearly reproducible effects apparent.

- Central nervous system responses to induced electric current should be further investigated including, for example, further volunteer studies of deficits induced in tests of visual processing, reasoning and memory, and *in vitro* brain slice studies of weak electric current effects.

- The possible increased susceptibility of some people to induced current, for example, those taking psychoactive drugs, epileptics etc., should be investigated. Such studies should be accompanied by appropriate dosimetric calculations.

- There is a particular need to coordinate studies of the possible carcinogenicity of electromagnetic fields, particularly at 50 Hz, within the EU. The experimental work should include co-carcinogenesis experiments, particularly looking at co-promotion in animal and cellular models, studies of effects on cell signalling and proliferation, Ca^{2+} uptake and gene expression, and further study of effects on melatonin and its possible role in the suppression of mammary tumour growth.

- Further investigations of possible weak field interaction mechanisms particularly of experimentally testable hypotheses such as magnetic field effects on radical pair interactions have merit. Further study of weak electromagnetic fields interactions with the optical system, in relation to effects on the production of melatonin by the pineal gland, should also be carried out.

8.1.3   Electromagnetic fields and radiation of frequencies between 100 kHz and 300 GHz

It seems probable that healthy people can tolerate body temperature rises of about 1°C. However, body temperatures should not exceed 38°C over prolonged periods. Animal data suggest that humans exposed acutely to RF radiation to the extent that body temperatures rise in excess of 1°C may show reduced mental performance, transient changes in circulating stress hormone levels, in the numbers of some circulating red blood cells and in some immune response.

Individual tissues of the body can be affected by RF and microwave induced rises in temperature. Areas of the brain such as the hypothalamus are sensitive to small changes in temperature and will initiate physiological responses such as those concerned with thermoregulation. Other tissues in the trunk and limbs are considered less sensitive. The developing embryo and fetus should also be regarded as vulnerable to raised temperature, localised temperature increases may result in developmental abnormalities including growth retardation. It is concluded that localised temperatures of up to 38°C in the head or in the developing embryo or fetus, 39°C in the neck and trunk and 40°C in the extremities are unlikely to produce adverse effects.

Many experimental data indicate that RF radiation is not mutagenic, consequently it is unlikely to act as an initiator of carcinogenesis. The few studies that have been carried out so far have looked mostly for evidence of an enhancement of the effect of spontaneous or chemically induced tumours. The results obtained are equivocal, although tumour progression may be enhanced at levels of exposure which may be thermally significant.

Pulsed RF radiation can have a number of specific effects, most of which can be avoided by restricting exposure levels to below the auditory threshold.

Recommendations

- There is further scope for the quantification of individual responses to whole body SARs. This would be particularly valuable in identifying the variation in individual susceptibilities within a population. In particular, magnetic resonance imaging centres, which process large numbers of patients, should be encouraged to record and publish data relating to whole-body responses to SAR. Data from experimental volunteer studies examining thermoregulatory responses to RF exposure combined with adverse environmental conditions and various rates of physical exercise would also be useful in this regard.

- Human auditory and other responses to pulsed microwave and modulated RF radiation should be further investigated.

- Few studies have examined the possible carcinogenicity of RF and microwave radiation. In view of the increasing use of various RF or microwave emitting devices there is scope for a modest, coordinated programme of investigation of the possible carcinogenic effects at appropriate frequencies.

8.1.4 Optical radiation

Exposure of the general public is dominated by solar radiation exposure even though the contribution from artificial sources has increased significantly over the past 30 years or so. Solar radiation exposure is clearly implicated in the increased incidence of skin cancer. There is little evidence to support the view that such increase as has already taken place is related to decreased levels of stratospheric ozone and consequential increases in solar UVR reaching the Earth's surface. A quantitative evaluation of risk for the induction of skin cancer requires a dose-response relationship to be established. The dose-response relationship and the carcinogenic spectral effectiveness of UVR for the induction of non-melanoma skin cancer in mice have been established but there are as yet few data relevant to the spectral effectiveness of UVR for the induction of malignant melanoma.

Many genetic and epigenetic factors play important roles in UVR-induced carcinogenesis. Xeroderma pigmentosum, an inherited syndrome, is an example of gene damage associated with increased sensitivity to skin cancer induction. Gene mutations responsible for different sensitivities, not necessarily correlated with other indicators of sensitivity, such as density of naevi and skin phototype, have not been completely identified.

Ultraviolet radiation can induce local or systemic response by affecting the immunological function of the skin. The skin, a major target for UVR, contains Langerhans' cells, keratinocytes and T cells, the cellular components of the peripheral immune system. Experimental work on animals has shown that low level exposure to UVR impairs the immune surveillance system at the site of exposure and higher levels of exposure suppress the immune system elsewhere also. These effects could have serious implications with respect to human health. Immune responses triggered by UVR exposure are only partly understood.

Cataract is a multifactorial disease related to the natural aging process. There is evidence that UVR can play a role in its onset and temporal progression. Photochemical reactions triggered by UV exposure, result in the production of free radicals and other oxidising chemical species.

- The implementation of test procedures to identify drugs, cosmetic and other substances that sensitise people to the effects of UVR should be supported.

- Studies on photobiological mechanisms of UVR-induced immune suppression should be supported.

- Studies on photobiological mechanisms of UVR-induced skin aging and UVR-induced degenerative effects on the ocular media should be supported.

- Basic biological research on skin cancer, particularly malignant melanoma, should be supported.

8.2   Epidemiological research

8.2.1   Electromagnetic fields and radiation

Some epidemiological reports present data indicative of an increase in cancer among children, adults and occupational groups. The current theoretical basis for the interaction of 50/60 Hz fields with living systems cannot explain such associations. Epidemiological studies have been reviewed by expert groups from a number of international and national bodies with responsibilities for radiation protection. The overall conclusions of different expert groups are similar, viz, although the results of more recent studies reflect some improvements in methodology, the data do not provide convincing evidence that electromagnetic fields and radiation are carcinogenic.

Recommendations

- Further efforts are clearly needed to determine whether exposure to magnetic fields or other factors in the residential environment may influence the risk of childhood cancer.

- There is an urgent need for large and statistically robust epidemiological studies based on objective measurements of exposure to electromagnetic fields. The feasibility of European-wide studies should be considered.

8.2.2   Optical radiation

The principal source of optical radiation with respect to public exposure is the sun and individual habits with respect to solar UVR exposure are important in the assessment of personal risk. Other sources which can represent a potential hazard to the general public are certain high power lasers in the public domain (particularly those used for entertainment and display), welding arcs (used without adequate personal protection in public situations) and certain lighting systems (where close proximity and/or high occupancy may be contributory factors to the total personal exposure, (for example, tungsten halogen lamps).

Recommendations

- Epidemiological research on skin cancer, particularly malignant melanoma, should be supported.

- Research is needed on the relationship with UVR exposure, especially in childhood, to numbers of, and presence of, abnormal types of naevi.

- Research is required into the relation of exposure to artificial sources of UVR, including sunbeds, to risks of malignant melanoma and non melanoma skin cancers.

- Epidemiological studies on UVR induced degenerative effects on the ocular media, and particularly cataract, should be supported.

- The possibility of European-wide studies should be considered.

8.3   Exposure and dosimetry research

8.3.1   Electromagnetic fields and radiation

The general public is exposed to electromagnetic fields arising from numerous sources generating a wide range of frequencies and modulations.

The principal sources of exposure at extremely low frequencies arise from the distribution and use of electric power. The highest electric field strengths at power frequencies to which members of the public are exposed arise close to high voltage overhead power lines whereas the highest magnetic field strengths arise close to various appliances.

At higher frequencies background exposure is mainly from broadcast and telecommunications sources. The antennas of high power television and radio at VHF and UHF frequencies are situated at heights above ground level such that members of the public are sufficiently remote from the source that they are not exposed to electric field strengths in excess of a few V m^{-1}.

Cellular telephone base station antennas are closer to the ground but are of lower power and whilst some cellular telephone base stations can potentially produce electric field strengths of tens of V m^{-1}, in practice measurements indicate field strengths at normally accessible positions of less than a V m^{-1}.

Transmitting stations operating at lower frequencies in the VLF to HF range can be significant sources of exposure but public access to the large sites is restricted. Radar, satellite links and high frequency point to point microwave communications systems are highly directive sources and as a result of their location and mode of operation do not normally present significant sources of public exposure.

The highest field strengths to which the public may be exposed at radiofrequencies are close to the antennas of relatively low power mobile and portable transmitters. However, exposure arising from the close approach of the body to antennas such as those used for mobile telephones cannot be ascertained on the basis of field strength measurements alone. The fields are highly non-uniform and in the reactive near-field of such devices it is necessary to ascertain the detailed way in which energy is absorbed in the body by using computer models or by carrying out measurements on physical models.

Recommendations

The sources reviewed in this document are extensive; however, the review has not identified every source of electric and magnetic fields to which people are or may be exposed.

- There is a need to be aware of the development of new technologies and the introduction of novel devices into the public domain which may materially affect the nature and the extent to which people may be exposed.

- Sources identified should be characterised in sufficient detail to enable exposure assessments to be carried out with respect to fundamental quantities restricting exposure. It should be recognised that spot environmental measurements may not completely characterise exposure in situations where the fields may be non-uniform and only partial body exposures arise.

- There is a need to further develop theoretical (computational) dosimetry based on anatomically and electrically realistic computational phantoms of the human body. This should be applied to determining internal fields and SARs resulting from exposure to external electric and magnetic fields and radiation.

- Support should be given to the dosimetric (computational and experimental) evaluation of SAR and temperature distribution within the body following localised or whole-body exposure.

- The use of personal exposure meters at 50 Hz power frequency should be encouraged to provide further information on the time distribution and magnitude of exposures. Such studies will enable specific sources contributing significantly to exposure to be identified and permit resources to be appropriately focused.

- There is a need for more information on the electromagnetic interference aspects of exposure to electric and magnetic fields.

- Information for the general public about levels of exposure to electromagnetic fields and human health should be developed and made available within the EU.

8.3.2 Optical radiation

The main source of optical radiation with respect to public exposure is the sun and individual habits with respect particularly to solar UVR exposure are important in the assessment of personal risk. Other sources which can represent a potential hazard to the general public are certain high power lasers (particularly those used for entertainment and display), welding arcs and certain lighting systems. However, published measurement data on sources appropriate to public exposures are limited, and it is recommended that further measurements on a wide range of sources encountered in the non-occupational environment are required to improve the data base for hazard assessment. In particular:

- A co-ordinated measurement network to assess environmental levels of solar radiation across Europe should be established to obtain reliable measurement data relating to the major source of public exposure from optical radiation.

- Support should be given to the dosimetric evaluation of personal exposure from solar UVR and in particular the distribution across the body for a variety of pursuits.

- More reliable data on the UVR, visible and IRR emissions of a wider range of artificial optical sources for hazard analysis need to be obtained, as many of the existing data stem from occupational exposure conditions in the 1970s and 1980s, and both the range of sources and exposure conditions are likely to have changed.

- With particular reference to UVR, more measurement information for health hazard assessment is required for sunbeds and solaria.

- With particular reference to visible and infrared radiation, more measurement information for health hazard assessment is required for common sources.

- With the development of laser technology, more measurement information for health hazard assessment is required for lasers used in the public domain and particularly for display and other entertainment lasers.

- The use of sunbeds should be discouraged as part of a public health awareness/education programme about UVR.

- Information for the general public and particularly for carers of children about the hazards of over exposure to UVR should be developed and made available within the EU.

8.4 Standards development

All guidelines that have been issued worldwide by different national and international organisations are based on preventing established effects on human health. In general, the formulation of guidelines for limiting exposure requires data from the fields of biology, epidemiology and dosimetry.

There is a large body of data related to the biological effects of electromagnetic fields, that has been critically evaluated in respect of the provision of exposure guidelines. International and national bodies have concluded that the data relating to the effect of electro-stimulation and heating solely form a basis for guidelines on limiting exposure.

Many epidemiological studies have been carried out especially on cancer induction in relation to exposure to electromagnetic fields. Careful evaluation of the results of such studies by international and national bodies led to the conclusion that these data currently cannot be used as a basis for setting limits of exposure for electromagnetic fields.

The principal role of dosimetry in establishing guidelines is in quantifying the interaction of external fields with biological systems. In this area significant progress has been made in applying both computational techniques as well as measurements based on well-understood physical interaction principles of fields with matter.

Recommendations

- It is important, that biological, epidemiological and dosimetric research relevant to the health effects of non-ionising radiation exposure is continuously reviewed by international and national bodies with responsibilities in radiation protection. Based on the results, guidance and limits of exposure should be revised if necessary. Scientific bodies should continue to rely only on scientific data relating to well-established health effects of non-ionising radiation.

- The development of health policies related to reducing the risks of exposure to non-ionising radiation will include decisions on political, economic and social aspects as well as on the scientific aspects. Within the EU, it would be preferable for such policies to be based on a wider international consensus.

European Commission

Non-ionizing radiation — Sources, exposure and health effects

Luxembourg: Office for Official Publications of the European Communities

1996 — IX, 163 pp. — 14.8 x 21.0 cm

ISBN 92-827-5492-8

Price (excluding VAT) in Luxembourg: ECU 17